Learning Genetic Algorithms with Python

Empower the Performance of
Machine Learning and AI Models with the
Capabilities of a Powerful Search Algorithm

Ivan Gridin

www.bpbonline.com

FIRST EDITION 2021

Copyright © BPB Publications, India

ISBN: 978-81-94837-756

Distributors:

BPB PUBLICATIONS
20, Ansari Road, Darya Ganj
New Delhi-110002
Ph: 23254990/23254991

DECCAN AGENCIES
4-3-329, Bank Street,
Hyderabad-500195
Ph: 24756967/24756400

MICRO MEDIA
Shop No. 5, Mahendra Chambers,
150 DN Rd. Next to Capital Cinema,
V.T. (C.S.T.) Station, MUMBAI-400 001
Ph: 22078296/22078297

BPB BOOK CENTRE
376 Old Lajpat Rai Market,
Delhi-110006
Ph: 23861747

To View Complete
BPB Publications Catalogue
Scan the QR Code:

Published by Manish Jain for BPB Publications, 20 Ansari Road, Darya Ganj, New Delhi-110002 and Printed by him at Repro India Ltd, Mumbai

www.bpbonline.com

Dedicated to :

My lovely little daughters: Ksenia and Elena.
Your endless love and energy charge me every day.

And to my beautiful and patient wife Tamara.
That's all thanks to you. You are the light of my life.

I love you

About the Author

Ivan Gridin is a Mathematician, Fullstack Developer, Data Scientist, and Machine Learning Expert living in Moscow, Russia. Over the years, he worked on distributive high-load systems and implemented different machine learning approaches in practice. One of the key areas of his research is the design and analysis of predictive time series models.

Ivan has fundamental math skills in probability theory, random process theory, time series analysis, machine learning, deep learning, and optimization. He also has in-depth knowledge and understanding of various programming languages such as Java, Python, PHP, and MATLAB.

Loving father, husband, and collector of old math books.

Linkedin: **http://www.linkedin.com/in/survex/**

About the Reviewer

Satyajeet Dhawale is a professional Data Scientist having a strong experience in machine learning, deep learning, computer vision, inferential and descriptive statistical analysis. He has worked on many projects that involve complex machine learning and deep learning algorithms and used a variety of data sets from a different domain. In his career, he has successfully delivered many machine learning and deep learning solutions for complex data problems. You can find more professional details about Satyajeet on LinkedIn. (**https://www.linkedin.com/in/satyajeet-dhawale/**)

Acknowledgement

There are a few people I want to thank for the idea and the motivation for writing this book. I thank my adorable wife Tamara; her patience and beauty inspired me every day. I thank my elder daughter Ksenia; her courage and determination motivated me in exhaustion moments. And my little daughter Elena for waking me up earlier – you're my energizer!

Thanks to my mom for her love and the genetics she gave me.

I am eternally grateful to my company AT Consulting. This company has done a lot to make me the specialist I am. And I especially want to thank Alexey Korotaev - one of the best managers I've ever seen. I'm proud to be a part of this big team.

Thanks to my friends, who helped me in all my endeavors. To Petr Rostov for his help in learning mathematics and programming. To my friend Yuri Babaev for his inspiration and humor that he brings into my life. To Denis Paramanov for sacrificing his vacation for my future wife and me. To Dmitry Suvorov for his effective gym workout. To Sergey Korsikov and Alena Gulyaeva for helping us to get used to this big city. This book would be impossible without all of them.

I want to give the warmest hugs to my new big family in Perm and Khabarovsk. I especially want to hug Konstantin Volosatov, the most handsome and intelligent policeman I have ever met, and his beautiful wife, Elena Volosatova. We love you all very much!

My gratitude also goes to the book reviewer Satyajeet Dhawale. His participation and useful advice have made this book much better.

Special thanks to BPB Publications for support, advice, and assistance in creating and publishing this book.

Preface

There is a lot of talk about Machine Learning, Deep Learning, Neural Networks, and many other terms and technologies that provides Artificial Intelligence in our life. These technologies are used everywhere in our daily life. Image and terrain recognition techniques are being used in autonomous vehicles that are already driving worldwide. And the number of autonomous cars is increasing at a tremendous rate.

Artificial intelligence frameworks and libraries are beginning to penetrate very deeply into all areas of programming. An ordinary programmer needs to have at least a basic understanding of what machine learning is, what kind of tasks it solves, and how to work with it. Machine learning contains a broad set of tools. Most of the books and teaching materials describe only a few of them, while the other approaches based on the evolutionary search for solving problems remain uncovered.

This book is about Genetic Algorithms. It tells how the principles formulated by Charles Darwin in his book "The Origin of Species" in 1859 in our time help to solve the most complex problems that contain billions and billions of solutions. Genetic Algorithms solve problems that cannot be solved analytically. It mimics the process of evolution and natural selection in a population, where each individual represents a solution to a problem. The more vital individuals from the population outlive the weaker ones and produce the next generation of individuals. So after the evolution process, after many generations, we get some solution to the problem, which will highly likely satisfy the requirements.

The main disadvantage of most machine learning tools can be formulated following way:

"They solve problems, but they don't solve the problem - how to solve problems."

Genetic algorithms provide a method for solving a problem, i.e., how to solve problems in the absence of human experience.

Genetic algorithms are a relatively simple and very effective method for solving a large class of problems. They are intuitive, simple, and can be an excellent introduction to machine learning.

The book consists of thirteen chapters, in which the reader will learn the following:

Chapter 1 is the introductory chapter giving the basic principles of evolution. It defines the genetic algorithm, the genetic algorithm's nature, its applicability, and the pros and cons.

Chapter 2 will discuss genetic algorithm architecture, its main logical concepts: individual, fitness function, population, selection, crossover, and mutation.

Chapter 3 will focus solely on the Selection method. It explains the selection in the sense of evolution, how it works, and how it affects the evolution process. We will cover the following selection methods: Tournament Selection, Proportional Selection, Stochastic universal sampling Selection, Rank Selection, Elite Selection.

Chapter 4 concentrates only on the Crossover operation. It describes the crossover, why it is important, how it works, and how it influences the solution search. We will study the following crossover methods: One Point Crossover, N-Point Crossover, Uniform Crossover, Linear Combination Crossover, Blend Crossover, Order Crossover, and Fitness Driven Crossover.

Chapter 5 discusses the last evolution operation called Mutation. Evolution would be impossible without the Mutation, and it is one of the most crucial parts of the genetic algorithm. Following mutation methods are discussed: Random Deviation Mutation, Exchange Mutation, Shift Mutation, Bit Flip Mutation, Inversion Mutation, Shuffle Mutation, and Fitness Driven Mutation.

Chapter 6. In this chapter, we will explore a way to compare the effectiveness of architectures of genetic algorithms. It defines what the best individual is. Explore the Genetic Algorithm as a random variable and cover the handy technique to compare two random variables called Monte-Carlo simulation.

Chapter 7 is the last theoretical chapter and is dedicated to parameter tuning. It shows how global parameters like population size, crossover, and mutation probability govern genetic algorithm flow dynamics. It studies each parameter influence and explains how each parameter affects the algorithm intuitively.

Chapter 8 starts the practical section of real-world problems. It covers one of the most common tasks - finding the black-box function's maxima. It covers which types of individuals can be created and design genetic algorithm architecture for this task.

Chapter 9 covers the first type of combinatorial problems, named binary encoded combinatorial problems. It designs the solution for the classical knapsack and schedule problem. And also, we will study a complex radar problem.

Chapter 10 studies the second type of combinatorial problem called ordered encoded combinatorial problems. Here we will discuss the traditional traveling salesman problem; also, we will investigate an original football manager problem.

Chapter 11 shows some other types of problems. It shows how to solve the general system of equations using genetic algorithms and another common graph coloring problem.

Chapter 12 brings the genetic algorithm to another level, from Machine Learning to Deep Learning. It shows how to design an adaptive genetic algorithm that can be used as a universal approach with self-tuning feature during the evolution process.

Chapter 13 is all about performance. It shows how to speed up the genetic algorithm with various techniques.

Downloading the code bundle and coloured images:

Please follow the link to download the
Code Bundle and the *Coloured Images* of the book:

https://rebrand.ly/6ad4a

All the chapters have associated code scripts in the book's Code Bundle.

Some parts required for the code to run may not be included in the text to save space. You should be able to run all of the code by yourself.

Errata

We take immense pride in our work at BPB Publications and follow best practices to ensure the accuracy of our content to provide with an indulging reading experience to our subscribers. Our readers are our mirrors, and we use their inputs to reflect and improve upon human errors, if any, that may have occurred during the publishing processes involved. To let us maintain the quality and help us reach out to any readers who might be having difficulties due to any unforeseen errors, please write to us at :

errata@bpbonline.com

Your support, suggestions and feedbacks are highly appreciated by the BPB Publications' Family.

Did you know that BPB offers eBook versions of every book published, with PDF and ePub files available? You can upgrade to the eBook version at www.bpbonline.com and as a print book customer, you are entitled to a discount on the eBook copy. Get in touch with us at :

business@bpbonline.com for more details.

At **www.bpbonline.com**, you can also read a collection of free technical articles, sign up for a range of free newsletters, and receive exclusive discounts and offers on BPB books and eBooks.

BPB is searching for authors like you

If you're interested in becoming an author for BPB, please visit **www.bpbonline.com** and apply today. We have worked with thousands of developers and tech professionals, just like you, to help them share their insight with the global tech community. You can make a general application, apply for a specific hot topic that we are recruiting an author for, or submit your own idea.

The code bundle for the book is also hosted on GitHub at **https://github.com/bpbpublications/Learning-Genetic-Algorithms-with-Python**. In case there's an update to the code, it will be updated on the existing GitHub repository.

We also have other code bundles from our rich catalog of books and videos available at **https://github.com/bpbpublications**. Check them out!

PIRACY

If you come across any illegal copies of our works in any form on the internet, we would be grateful if you would provide us with the location address or website name. Please contact us at **business@bpbonline.com** with a link to the material.

If you are interested in becoming an author

If there is a topic that you have expertise in, and you are interested in either writing or contributing to a book, please visit **www.bpbonline.com**.

REVIEWS

Please leave a review. Once you have read and used this book, why not leave a review on the site that you purchased it from? Potential readers can then see and use your unbiased opinion to make purchase decisions, we at BPB can understand what you think about our products, and our authors can see your feedback on their book. Thank you!

For more information about BPB, please visit **www.bpbonline.com**.

Table of Contents

CHAPTER 1
Introduction

As we know, evolution is one of the most perfect adaptation mechanisms. It is a way to achieve extraordinary and complex solutions. Understanding the principles of evolution gave us a new approach called **genetic algorithms**. We will now explore this rather beautiful, simple, and effective approach to problem-solving.

Structure

In this chapter, we will discuss the following topics:

- Nature of genetic algorithm
- Applicability of genetic algorithms
- Pros and cons of genetic algorithms
- Your first genetic algorithm

1.1 Nature of genetic algorithm

The rapid development in AI is made possible for humans to obtain solution to abstract problems. Complex computational problems that are very difficult to solve by classical methods can now be solved by AI.

One of the most powerful techniques to solve such complex problems is **genetic algorithms (GA),** which is based on the principle of an evolutionary approach.

In the late 60s, American researcher *J. Holland* proposed to find solutions to optimization problems using methods and evolution models of animal populations in nature. Since the evolution's basic laws were investigated and described by genetics, the proposed approach was called genetic algorithms. GA is a randomly directed search algorithm based on mechanisms of natural selection and natural genetics. It implements the principle of survival of the fittest, forming and changing the search algorithm based on evolutionary modeling.

The basic steps in natural evolution are as follows:

- **Selection:** According to *Charles Darwin*, natural selection laws were formulated in the book *On the Origin of Species*. The central postulate is that *individuals who can better solve problems, survive and reproduce more*. In GAs, each individual is a solution to some problem. According to this principle, individuals who solve the problem better have a greater chance of surviving and leaving offsprings.

- **Crossover:** This means that the offspring chromosome is made up of parts that are derived from the parents' chromosomes. This principle was discovered in 1865 by *G. Mendel*.

- **Mutation:** In 1900, *H. de Vries* discovered the principle of random change. Initially, this term was used to describe significant changes in descendants' properties that were not present in their parents. By analogy, genetic algorithms use a similar mechanism to change offspring's properties, thereby increasing individuals' diversity in a population.

Genetic algorithms have the following characteristics:

- Easy to implement
- Used for a wide range of tasks
- They do not require any additional information about the nature of the problem
- Easy and convenient to parallelize

1.2 Applicability of genetic algorithms

As a solution, the GA tries to find the extremum of some function that characterizes the quality of the solution to the problem. Generally, the GA does not guarantee that the solution found is the best of all that's possible. Usually, this is not required, but it is only important that the found solution satisfies the meaning of the problem being solved.

The areas of application of GAs include the following:

- Search for extremum of various functions
- Finding the shortest paths (traveling salesman problem)

- Combinatorial optimization
- Tasks of placement and scheduling
- Automatic programming tasks
- AI tasks (choosing the structure and parameters of artificial neural networks)

In real time scenarios, GAs are used to develop AI systems, like designing tasks for aircraft routes at airports, finding the optimal behavior of robots, problems of constructing investment portfolios, and so on.

1.3 Pros and cons of genetic algorithms

Like any other approach to problem-solving, GAs have their pros and cons as well. Understanding these features will allow you to solve the practical problems in a better way.

The pros of genetic algorithms are as follows:

- **A wide range of tasks to be solved:** GA is successfully applied in the following areas – combinatorial optimization, finance (portfolio optimization), machine learning (feature extraction, neural network hyper-parameter optimization), code-breaking, game theory, natural sciences, and so on.

- **Ease of implementation:** The algorithm implies the presence of steps – natural selection, crossing, and mutation. This conceptual simplicity makes this method available to a wide range of developers.

- **Resistance to dynamic changes in problem conditions:** The GA is able to retrain if the conditions of the problem change when searching for a solution.

- **The ability for self-adaptation:** GAs are able, after a certain period of evolution, to adapt to the conditions of the problem being solved.

- **Ease of scaling:** Can easily be used on big data where the data is spread over the distributed systems. GAs, as a highly parallel process, can be easily parallelized, which makes it possible to proportionally accelerate the finding of a solution with an increase in computing power.

- **Solving problems for which there is no solution experience:** One of the biggest advantages of GAs is their ability to investigate problems for which there is no relevant solution experience. It should be noted that expert assessments are often used to solve difficult-to-formalize problems, but they sometimes give less acceptable solutions than automated methods.

The cons of genetic algorithms are as follows:

- The complexity of representing an individual in a population and determining the fitness function.

- For real problems, it is initially not-at-all obvious in what form it is necessary to present a set of individual genes for a successful solution to the problem, and also determine the assessment of the quality of a particular individual.

- The choice of parameters of the architecture of the GA.

- There are no effective criteria for the termination of the algorithm.

- Not effective for finding an extremum for smooth functions with one extremum.

- They require large enough computing resources.

- When solving problems, there are cases of premature convergence, and therefore, generally, they do not guarantee in finding the global extremum.

1.4 Your first genetic algorithm

Well, let's try to build our first GA solution. We will start from a trivial example which shows us the basics.

Let's say we have the following function, *sin(x) - 0.2 * abs(x)*. Refer to the following *figure 1.1:*

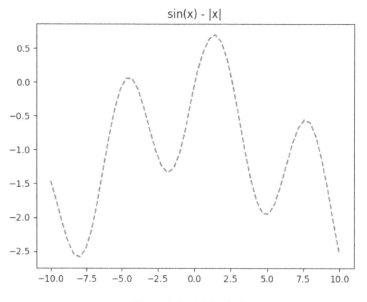

Figure 1.1: *sin(x) - |x|*

We will find the maxima of the preceding function.

This function has several local maximums. All individuals in the population in our GA will try to climb as high as possible.

Let's see the GA in action. Execute the following code (we will cover the details in future chapters) ch1/your_first_genetic_algorithm.py :

Import part

```
import random

from typing import List

import numpy as np

import matplotlib.pyplot as plt
```

Auxiliary GA operations

```
def _utils_constraints(g, min, max):
    if max and g > max:
        g = max
    if min and g < min:
        g = min
    return g


def crossover_blend(g1, g2, alpha, min = None, max = None):
    shift = (1. + 2. * alpha) * random.random() - alpha
    new_g1 = (1. - shift) * g1 + shift * g2
    new_g2 = shift * g1 + (1. - shift) * g2

    return _utils_constraints(new_g1, min, max), _utils_constraints(new_g2, min, max)


def mutate_gaussian(g, mu, sigma, min = None, max = None):
    mutated_gene = g + random.gauss(mu, sigma)
    return _utils_constraints(mutated_gene, min, max)


def select_tournament(population, tournament_size):
    new_offspring = []
    for _ in range(len(population)):
        candidates = [random.choice(population) for _ in range(tournament_size)]
        new_offspring.append(max(candidates, key = lambda ind: ind.fitness))
    return new_offspring
```

```python
def func(x):
    return np.sin(x) - .2 * abs(x)


def get_best(population):
    best = population[0]
    for ind in population:
        if ind.fitness > best.fitness:
            best = ind
    return best


def plot_population(population, number_of_population):
    best = get_best(population)
    x = np.linspace(-10, 10)
    plt.plot(x, func(x), '--', color = 'blue')
    plt.plot([ind.get_gene() for ind in population], [ind.fitness for ind
in population], 'o', color = 'orange')
    plt.plot([best.get_gene()], [best.fitness], 's', color = 'green')
    plt.title(f"Generation number {number_of_population}")
    plt.show()
    plt.close()
```

Individual class

```python
class Individual:

    def __init__(self, gene_list: List[float]) -> None:
        self.gene_list = gene_list
        self.fitness = func(self.gene_list[0])

    def get_gene(self):
        return self.gene_list[0]

    @classmethod
    def crossover(cls, parent1, parent2):
        child1_gene, child2_gene = crossover_blend(parent1.get_gene(),
parent2.get_gene(), 1, -10, 10)
        return Individual([child1_gene]), Individual([child2_gene])


    @classmethod
```

```
def mutate(cls, ind):
    mutated_gene = mutate_gaussian(ind.get_gene(), 0, 1, -10, 10)
    return Individual([mutated_gene])


@classmethod
def select(cls, population):
    return select_tournament(population, tournament_size = 3)


@classmethod
def create_random(cls):
    return Individual([random.randrange(-1000, 1000) / 100])
```

GA flow

```
random.seed(52)
# random.seed(16)  # local maximum
POPULATION_SIZE = 10
CROSSOVER_PROBABILITY = .8
MUTATION_PROBABILITY = .1
MAX_GENERATIONS = 10

first_population = [Individual.create_random() for _ in range(POPULATION_
SIZE)]
plot_population(first_population, 0)

generation_number = 0

population = first_population.copy()

while generation_number < MAX_GENERATIONS:

    generation_number += 1

    # SELECTION
    offspring = Individual.select(population)

    # CROSSOVER
    crossed_offspring = []
    for ind1, ind2 in zip(offspring[::2], offspring[1::2]):
        if random.random() < CROSSOVER_PROBABILITY:
            kid1, kid2 = Individual.crossover(ind1, ind2)
```

```
        crossed_offspring.append(kid1)
        crossed_offspring.append(kid2)
    else:
        crossed_offspring.append(ind1)
        crossed_offspring.append(ind2)

# MUTATION
mutated_offspring = []
for mutant in crossed_offspring:
    if random.random() < MUTATION_PROBABILITY:
        new_mutant = Individual.mutate(mutant)
        mutated_offspring.append(new_mutant)
    else:
        mutated_offspring.append(mutant)

population = mutated_offspring.copy()

plot_population(population, generation_number)
```

Now, let's examine how individuals of each population behave during each generation. Refer to the following graphs:

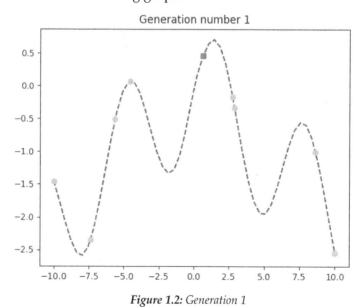

Figure 1.2: Generation 1

In the preceding *figure 1.2*, the first-generation is just the random distribution of points on the curve. We denote the green point as the highest.

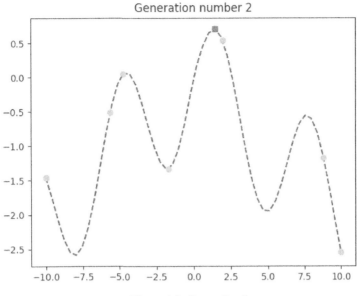

Figure 1.3: *Generation 2*

The second generation, as shown in the preceding *figure 1.3*, produces an individual on the top of the highest hill. But let's see how other individuals will behave.

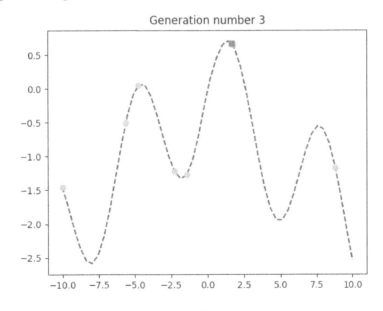

Figure 1.4: *Generation 3*

The third generation, as shown in the preceding *figure 1.4*, shows an interesting situation. The highest point moved a little bit right from the top. This behavior is typical for genetic algorithms. Evolution is the constant search for the best solution; it always explores the nearest area trying to offer another slightly different mechanism that suits better.

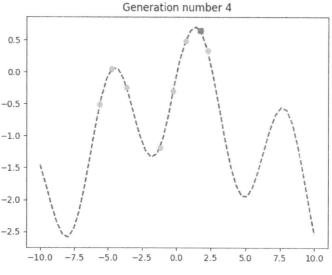

Figure 1.5: *Generation 4*

In the fourth generation, as shown in the preceding *figure 1.5*, we see how the entire population begins to strive for the individual that is at the top. The most successful individual in several generations managed to share their genes with other members of the population, which made them look like themselves.

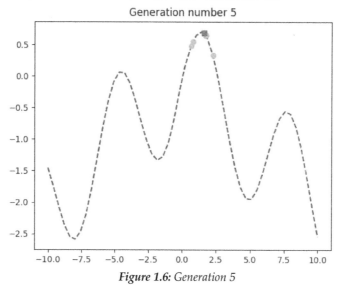

Figure 1.6: *Generation 5*

Closer! Almost all population individuals has reached the top, as shown in the preceding *figure 1.6*.

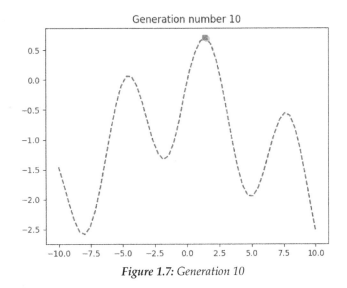

Figure 1.7: *Generation 10*

After 10 generations, all individuals of the population are in the most optimal position for themselves, as shown in the preceding *figure 1.7.*

NOTE: GA is random by its nature, and by itself, it cannot guarantee the best solution (that is, global maxima)! We will cover different techniques trying to maximize this probability, but it is important to understand that GA finds local, but not global maxima.

Let's see the random behavior of our solution, uncomment following line in the preceding script:

```
# random.seed(16)  # local maximum
```

We have the following final distribution of population:

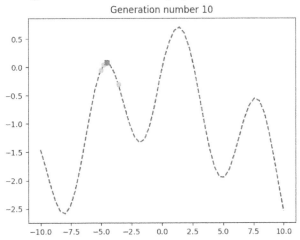

Figure 1.8: *Generation 10 with local maxima*

In the case of our problem, this is very unlikely, but it can happen. In future chapters, we will cover the details of the algorithm we used here.

Conclusion

In this chapter, we began our acquaintance with genetic algorithms, how this approach relates to the principles of evolution and natural selection. We examined the operation of this algorithm in action with a specific example.

In the next chapter, we will continue our study and consider the basic logical blocks and the structure of genetic algorithms.

Questions

1. Genetic algorithms always guarantees to find the best solution. Is it true?

2. One of the most important features of genetic algorithms is to find a solution to a problem without any accumulated experience. Is that true?

3. How would you formulate the basic principles of natural selection?

CHAPTER 2
Genetic Algorithm Flow

The modern understanding of evolution is based on the Darwin theory and genetics. The mechanism of natural selection is known as the process of ensuring the stability and adaptation of species. Strong and viable individuals survive, leaving offspring, to whom their characteristics are passed on. Weak individuals, on the contrary, perish without participating in reproduction.

A genetic algorithm is an approach that mimics the evolutionary search process. But what is evolution? What steps and stages does it consist of? In this chapter, we will look at the basic logical blocks of the genetic algorithm flow.

Structure

In this chapter, we will discuss the following topics:

- Individual
- Fitness function
- Population
- Selection
- Crossover
- Mutation
- Genetic algorithm flow

2.1 Individual

An individual is an object that represents a solution to a problem. The response parameters are determined by the genes that are contained in the individual.

Usually, there are two ways to create individuals:

- Random generation of an individual
- Creating an individual with a specified set of genes

In the case of our problem from *Chapter 1: Introduction,* an individual is represented as follows `ch2/individual.py` :

Import part

```
import random

from ch2.fitness import fitness
from ch2.settings import MIN_BORDER, MAX_BORDER
```

Individual class

```
class Individual:

    def __init__(self, gene_list, fitness_function) -> None:
        self.gene_list = gene_list
        self.fitness = fitness_function(self.gene_list[0])

    def __str__(self) -> str:
        return f"{self.gene_list[0]:.2f} -> {self.fitness:.2f}"

    def get_gene(self):
        return self.gene_list[0]
```

Individual creation

```
def create_random_individual():
    return Individual([random.uniform(MIN_BORDER, MAX_BORDER)], fitness)

def create_individual(gene):
    return Individual([gene], fitness)
```

ch2/settings.py:

```
MIN_BORDER = -10
MAX_BORDER = 10
```

Here are some examples of typical problems and their solutions presented by individuals.

Multivariable function

Let's say we have two-variables function, *f(x,y)*, as shown in the following *figure 2.1:*

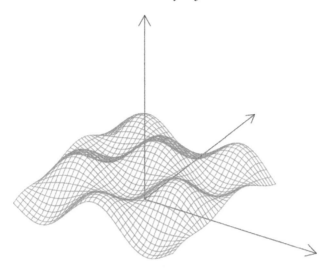

Figure 2.1: *Two-variables function*

If we are going to find the maxima of this function, then an individual will be represented as a pair (x,y).

Traveling salesman problem

We have seven cities on the map, as shown in the following *figure 2.2:*

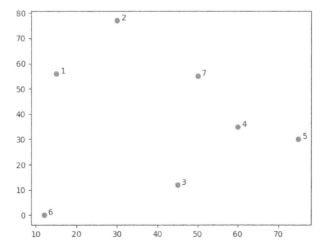

Figure 2.2: *7 cities on the map*

If we need to find the shortest way to visit all seven cities, then an individual will be represented as a sequence of numbers (1, 2, 3, 4, 5, 6, 7). For example, this individual (7, 2, 3, 6, 1, 4, 5) is describing this route, as shown in the following *figure 2.3:*

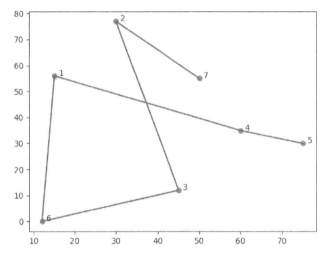

Figure 2.3: Route (7, 2, 3, 6, 1, 4, 5)

Each task requires the formation of its own individual. Sometimes the structure of an individual can be quite complex.

2.2 Fitness function

The fitness function is equivalent to the natural concept of the fitness of a living organism. This function characterizes how well an individual is adapted to the environment.

Depending on the problem to be solved, the best individual is considered to be the one whose objective function is maxima or minima.

For our problem of finding the maxima of sin (x) - 0.5 |x|, the best individual will be the one with the maxima fitness function.

Let's consider an example of calculating the fitness function `ch2/fitness.py`:

Fitness function

```
def fitness(x):
    return np.sin(x) - .2 * abs(x)
```

Fitness of an individual

```
if __name__ == '__main__':
    from ch2.individual import Individual
```

```
ind = Individual([1], fitness)
print(f"Individual fitness: {ind.fitness}")
```

Result
```
0.6414709848078965
```

2.3 Population

A population is just a set of individuals. When we say that we are creating a random population, it means that we are simply creating a certain number of random individuals.

For each population, the following characteristics can be obtained:

- **Best individual:** The best individual is the individual that has the maximum fitness function value.
- **Best fitness:** The best fitness is the value fitness function that the best individual has.
- **Average fitness:** The average fitness value is the average fitness function value for all individuals in the population.

Let's build a population of 10 random individuals and evaluate its characteristics ch2/population.py:

Import part
```
import random
import numpy as np
import matplotlib.pyplot as plt


from ch2.individual import create_random_individual
from ch2.fitness import fitness
from ch2.settings import MIN_BORDER, MAX_BORDER
```

Population methods
```
def get_best_individual(population):
    return max(population, key = lambda ind: ind.fitness)

def get_average_fitness(population):
    return sum([i.fitness for i in population]) / len(population)
```

Plotting the population on fitness curve
```
def plot_population(population):
        # best individual from the population
```

```python
    best_ind = get_best_individual(population)

    # fitness of the best individual
    best_fitness = best_ind.fitness

    # average fitness of the population
    average_fitness = get_average_fitness(population)

    # plotting fitness curve
    x = np.linspace(MIN_BORDER, MAX_BORDER)
    plt.plot(x, fitness(x), '--', color = 'blue')

    # plotting whole population
    plt.plot(
        [ind.get_gene() for ind in population],
        [ind.fitness for ind in population],
        'o', color = 'orange'
    )

    # plotting best individual
    plt.plot(
        [best_ind.get_gene()], [best_ind.fitness],
        's', color = 'green')

    # population average fitness
    plt.plot(
        [MIN_BORDER, MAX_BORDER],
        [average_fitness, average_fitness],
        color = 'grey'
    )
    plt.title(f"Best Individual: {best_ind}, Best Fitness: {best_
fitness:.2f} \n "
            f"Average Population Fitness: {average_fitness:.2f}"
            )
    plt.show()
```

Initialization of population

```
if __name__ == '__main__':
    # PARAMETER: the size of initial population
    POPULATION_SIZE = 10
    random.seed(22)

    # Generating random population
    population = [create_random_individual() for _ in range(POPULATION_
SIZE)]

    # plotting the distribution of the population on fitness curve
    plot_population(population)
```

Let's take a look at the following *figure 2.4*, to understand the visualization of random population:

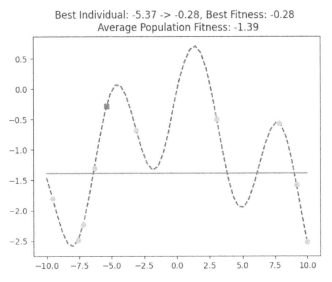

Figure 2.4: *Visualization of random population*

2.4 Selection

Selection is necessary to select more adapted individuals for crossing.

NOTE: Selection is the first genetic operation to be performed on a population. As a result of selection, the individuals that are selected will participate in the process of generating a new population.

Selection itself does not generate the new population; it is only responsible for selecting individuals that can leave the offspring.

As an example, consider tournament selection, where one must choose three different random individuals from the population, and from these three, they choose the best one.

Details of the selection mechanisms will be discussed in *Chapter 3: Selection*.

ch2/selection.py:

Tournament selection method

```python
def select_tournament(population, tournament_size):
    new_offspring = []
    for _ in range(len(population)):
        candidates = [random.choice(population) for _ in range(tournament_size)]
        new_offspring.append(max(candidates, key = lambda ind: ind.fitness))
    return new_offspring
```

Applying selection to random population

```python
if __name__ == '__main__':

    random.seed(29)

    # PARAMETER: the size of initial population
    POPULATION_SIZE = 5

    # Generating random population
    generation_1 = [create_random_individual() for _ in range(POPULATION_SIZE)]

    # Population after applying selection
    generation_2 = select_tournament(generation_1, 3)

    # Printing results
    print("Generation 1")
    [print(ind) for ind in generation_1]

    print("Generation 2")
    [print(ind) for ind in generation_2]
```

Result

```
Generation 1
0.96 -> 0.63
-3.08 -> -0.67
6.90 -> -0.80
-4.23 -> 0.04
0.21 -> 0.16

Generation 2
-4.23 -> 0.04
0.96 -> 0.63
-4.23 -> 0.04
0.96 -> 0.63
0.21 -> 0.16
```

As you can see from the example, the most adapted individuals were admitted to selection.

2.5 Crossover

Crossover is the process of generating new offspring. The main purpose of crossover is the exchange of genetic information, and to transfer the accumulated experience to the offspring. The child should not be very different from the parents.

Crossover mechanisms will be discussed in detail in *Chapter 4, Crossover.*

Consider an example of crossover, called *blending*, in which we take the gene of both parents, and randomly select the gene of the child in the range that is determined by the genes of the parents.

`ch2/crossover.py`:

Import part

```python
import random
import numpy as np
import matplotlib.pyplot as plt


from ch2.individual import create_random_individual, create_individual
from ch2.fitness import fitness
from ch2.settings import MIN_BORDER, MAX_BORDER
```

Crossover implementation

```python
def gene_constraints(g, min_ = MIN_BORDER, max_ = MAX_BORDER):
    """

    Limits gene value inside interval [min_, max_]
    """

    if max_ and g > max_:
        g = max_
    if min_ and g < min_:
        g = min_
    return g


def crossover_blend(g1, g2, alpha = 0.3):
    """

    Gene blending. Explained in Chapter 4. Crossover
    """

    shift = (1. + 2. * alpha) * random.random() - alpha
    new_g1 = (1. - shift) * g1 + shift * g2
    new_g2 = shift * g1 + (1. - shift) * g2


    return gene_constraints(new_g1), gene_constraints(new_g2)

def crossover(ind1, ind2):
    """

    Individual crossover
    """

    offspring_genes = crossover_blend(ind1.get_gene(), ind2.get_gene())
    return [create_individual(offspring_genes[0]),
            create_individual(offspring_genes[1])]
```

Applying crossover to random individuals

```python
if __name__ == '__main__':
    random.seed(30)

    # Pair of random individuals
    p_1 = create_random_individual()
    p_2 = create_random_individual()

    # Offspring of individuals
```

```
offspring = crossover(p_1, p_2)

c_1 = offspring[0]
c_2 = offspring[1]

# Visualization
x = np.linspace(MIN_BORDER, MAX_BORDER)
plt.plot(x, fitness(x), '--', color = 'blue')
plt.plot(
    [p_1.get_gene(), p_2.get_gene()],
    [p_1.fitness, p_2.fitness],
    'o', markersize = 15, color = 'orange'
)
plt.plot(
    [c_1.get_gene(), c_2.get_gene()],
    [c_1.fitness, c_2.fitness],
    's', markersize = 15, color = 'green'
)
plt.title("Circle : Parents, Square: Children")
plt.show()
```

Let's take a look at the following *figure 2.5* for an understanding of crossover:

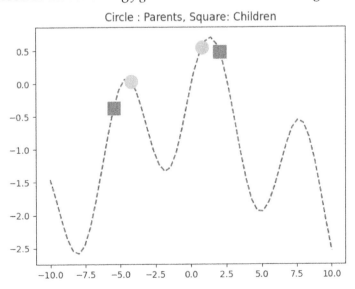

Figure 2.5: Crossover

2.6 Mutation

Mutation is a random change that an individual's genes undergo. Mutation is the factor that drives the development of evolution. Each child contains something that neither of his parents has. Mutation is the most important factor in evolution, which allows you to find new solutions.

If the trees begin to grow taller, then a child of a horse, whose neck is slightly longer than its parents, will be able to find food for itself more easily, which means it will be more adapted to life and will be able to pass on this feature to its offspring. This is exactly how, by accumulating positive mutations from generation to generation, a horse can evolve into a giraffe.

More on the mechanisms of mutations will be discussed in *Chapter 5: Mutation*.

Let's consider a mutation example. A mutation will be implemented by adding a random variable with a normal distribution with mean 0 and sigma 1.

`ch2/mutate.py`:

Import part

```
import random
import numpy as np
import matplotlib.pyplot as plt


from ch2.individual import create_random_individual, create_individual
from ch2.fitness import fitness
from ch2.settings import MIN_BORDER, MAX_BORDER
```

Mutation implementation

```
def gene_constraints(g, min_ = MIN_BORDER, max_ = MAX_BORDER):
    """

    Limits gene value inside interval [min_, max_]
    """

    if max_ and g > max_:
        g = max_
    if min_ and g < min_:
        g = min_
    return g


def mutate_gaussian(g, mu, sigma):
    """
```

```
    Gaussian Mutation. Explained in Chapter 5. Mutation
    """

    mutated_gene = g + random.gauss(mu, sigma)
    return gene_constraints(mutated_gene)

def mutate(ind):
    """

    Mutation of Individual
    """

    return create_individual(mutate_gaussian(ind.get_gene(), 0, 1))
```

Applying mutation to random individual

```
if __name__ == '__main__':

    random.seed(37)

    # Random Individual
    individual = create_random_individual()

    # Mutated Individual
    mutated = mutate(individual)

    # Visualization
    x = np.linspace(MIN_BORDER, MAX_BORDER)
    plt.plot(x, fitness(x), '--', color = 'blue')
    plt.plot(
        [individual.get_gene()],
        [individual.fitness],
        'o', markersize = 20, color = 'orange'
    )
    plt.plot(
        [mutated.get_gene()],
        [mutated.fitness],
        's', markersize = 20, color = 'green'
    )
    plt.title("Circle : Before Mutation, Square: After Mutation")
    plt.show()
```

Let's take a look at the following *figure 2.6* for an understanding of mutation:

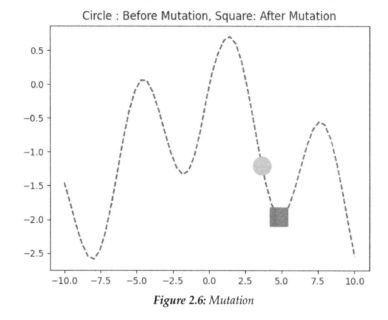

Figure 2.6: *Mutation*

2.7 Genetic algorithm flow

Let's put this all together! The whole GA flow looks like how it appears in the following *figure 2.7:*

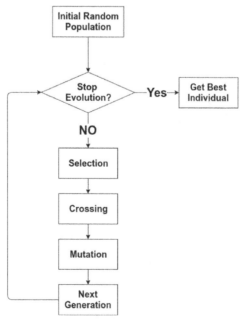

Figure 2.7: *Genetic Algorithm Flow*

There are various conditions for stopping the GA, for example:

- Finding an acceptable solution
- Reaching a certain number of generations
- Decrease in qualitative improvements in the population

In our example, GA will simply stop after 10 generations.

Genetic algorithm has special parameters:

- **Crossover probability:** The probability of crossing.
- **Mutation probability:** The probability of mutation.

  ```
  ch2/genetic_algorithm_flow.py:
  ```

Import part

```python
import random

from ch2.crossover import crossover
from ch2.individual import create_random_individual
from ch2.mutate import mutate
from ch2.population import plot_population
from ch2.selection import select_tournament
```

Example of genetic algorithm flow

```python
if __name__ == '__main__':

    # PARAMETERS
    POPULATION_SIZE = 10
    CROSSOVER_PROBABILITY = .8
    MUTATION_PROBABILITY = .1
    MAX_GENERATIONS = 10

    random.seed(29)

    # Initial random population
    population = [create_random_individual() for _ in range(POPULATION_SIZE)]

    for generation_number in range(POPULATION_SIZE):
        # SELECTION OPERATION
        selected = select_tournament(population, 3)
        # CROSSOVER
        crossed_offspring = []
        for ind1, ind2 in zip(selected[::2], selected[1::2]):
```

```
        if random.random() < CROSSOVER_PROBABILITY:
            # Applying crossover to pair of individuals
            children = crossover(ind1, ind2)
            crossed_offspring.append(children[0])
            crossed_offspring.append(children[1])
        else:
            # Passing individuals further without crossover
            crossed_offspring.append(ind1)
            crossed_offspring.append(ind2)

# MUTATION
mutated = []
for ind in crossed_offspring:
    if random.random() < MUTATION_PROBABILITY:
        # Applying mutation to an individual
        mutated.append(mutate(ind))
    else:
        # Passing individual further without mutation
        mutated.append(ind)

# Next generation
population = mutated

plot_population(population)
```

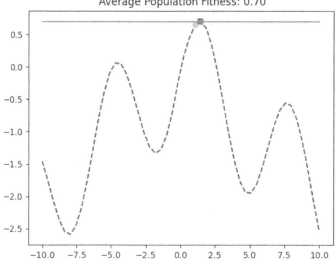

Figure 2.8: Result of Genetic Algorithm

The preceding *figure 2.8* shows the result of genetic algorithm, and as expected, after 10 generations, all individuals settled in the most favorable place for them. And the best solution to our problem is 1.4; with this value the function sin (x) - 0.5 |x| reaches 0.71.

Conclusion

We examined step by step what a genetic algorithm is. We covered evolutionary concepts – individual, fitness function, population, selection, crossing, mutation. And as a result, we have found the solution to the problem of finding the maxima of the function sin (x) - 0.5 |x| using a genetic algorithm.

In the following chapters, we will take a closer look at the operations – selection, crossing, and mutation.

Points to remember

- **GA flow consists of the following steps:** Initialization of random population, selection, crossover, and mutation.
- **GA has the following tunable parameters:** Population size, crossover probability, mutation probability, and maximum number of generations.

Multiple choice questions

1. We want to find the minima of the function sin(x) – 0.5|x|. What will the fitness function look like?

    a) sin(x)

    b) sin(x) – 0.5 |x|

    c) |x|

    d) sin(x) + 0.5 |x|

2. We want to find the minima of the function sin(x) – 0.5|x|. How will we determine the best individual?

    a) Individual with highest fitness function: sin(x) – 0.5|x|

    b) Individual with lowest fitness function: sin(x) – 0.5|x|

3. What is the correct sequence of steps in GA flow?

    a) crossover, selection, mutation

    b) mutation, crossover, selection

    c) selection, crossover, mutation

    d) selection, mutation, crossover

Answers

1. b
2. b
3. c

Questions

1. Say we have two individuals ind1 and ind2. And ind1.fitness is lower than ind2.fitness. After tournament selection ind1 is selected, but ind2 is not. Is this possible?

2. What happens if we remove the mutation from our genetic algorithm? (MUTATION_PROBABILITY = 0) How will the search process change?

Key terms

- **Individual:** Represents a solution to the problem.
- **Population:** It is the set of individuals.
- **Fitness function:** It is a measure of how well an individual solves a problem.
- **Selection:** The process of selecting individuals for crossover.
- **Crossover:** It is a generation of new offspring.
- **Mutation:** It is the random gene change of an individual.

CHAPTER 3
Selection

Selection is the choice of those individuals that will participate in creating offspring for the next population, that is, for the next generation. Such a choice is made by the principle of natural selection, according to which the most adapted individuals have the highest chances of participating in the creation of new individuals. As a result, an intermediate population (or parent pool) appears. An intermediate population is a set of individuals that have acquired the right to breed. Adapted individuals can be recorded there several times. The *abandoned* individuals will most likely not get there at all.

NOTE: It is important to understand that the same individual can be selected several times by the selection method, which means it can repeatedly participate in the process of creating new individuals.

Structure

In this chapter, we will look at the following selection methods:

- Tournament selection
- Proportional selection
- Stochastic universal sampling selection
- Rank selection
- Elite selection

Objectives

- Introduce basic selection methods
- Understand key features of each method
- Get practical examples

3.1 Tournament selection

Tournament selection is one of the simplest selection methods, and we will start with it. In tournament selection, a subgroup is selected in a population, and then the best individual in this subgroup is selected. Typically, the size of a subgroup is 2 or 3 individuals.

Tournament selection method can be illustrated by the following script `ch3/demo_ selection_tournament.py`:

Import part

```
import random
import pandas as pd
import matplotlib.pyplot as plt
from ch3.individual import Individual
```

Tournament selection

```
POPULATION_SIZE = 10
TOURNAMENT_SIZE = 3

population = Individual.create_random_population(POPULATION_SIZE)
candidates = [random.choice(population) for _ in range(TOURNAMENT_SIZE)]
best = [max(candidates, key = lambda ind: ind.fitness)]
```

Visualization

```
def plot_individuals(individual_set):
    df = pd.DataFrame({
        'name':    [ind.name for ind in individual_set],
        'fitness': [ind.fitness for ind in individual_set]
    })
    df.plot.bar(x = 'name', y = 'fitness', rot = 0)
    plt.show()

plot_individuals(population)
plot_individuals(candidates)
plot_individuals(best)
```

Let's take a look at the following *figure 3.1* for visualization of random population with fitness function:

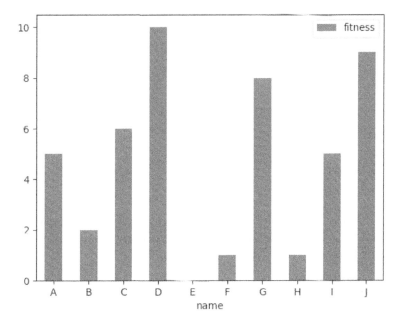

Figure 3.1: *Visualization of random population with fitness function*

Say, we have the population as shown in the preceding figure, and we randomly choose three individuals from it – A, I, D (refer to the following *figure 3.2*):

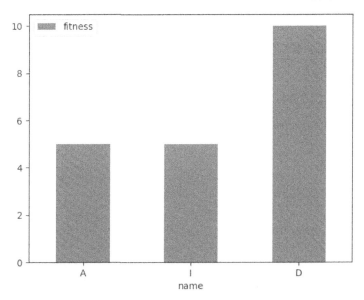

Figure 3.2: *Visualization of selected subgroup: A, I, D*

And as a result, the D individual is chosen.

The tournament selection can be implemented the following way ch3/ `selection_tournament.py`:

import random

```
def selection_tournament(individuals, group_size = 2):
    selected = []
    for _ in range(len(individuals)):
        candidates = [random.choice(individuals) for _ in range(group_
size)]
        selected.append(max(candidates, key = lambda ind: ind.fitness))
    return selected
```

> **NOTE: It is worth mentioning that if the group size is two, then the worst individual will never be selected; if the group size is three, then the two worst individuals will never be selected, and so on.**

Let's see this method in action ch3/`example_selection_tournament.py`:

```
import random
from ch3.selection_tournament import selection_tournament
from ch3.individual import Individual

POPULATION_SIZE = 5
random.seed(4)

population = Individual.create_random_population(POPULATION_SIZE)
selected = selection_tournament(population, group_size = 3)

print(f"Population: {population}")
print(f"Selected: {selected}")
```

Result

```
Population: [A: 3, B: 4, C: 1, D: 6, E: 7]
Selected: [B: 4, E: 7, B: 4, E: 7, B: 4]
```

As expected, two worst individuals, A and C were not selected. But we have one more interesting result – the individual D, which has the second fitness score, was also not selected. You always have to keep in mind that the tournament selection is a random process, and there is no 100% guarantee that the best individual will be selected.

3.2 Proportional selection

This method can be illustrated with a roulette wheel. Each individual is assigned a sector of the roulette wheel, the value of which is set proportional to the value of the fitness function of a given individual; therefore, the greater the value of the fitness function, the larger the sector on the roulette wheel. From this, it follows that the larger the sector on the roulette wheel, the higher the chance that this particular individual will be chosen.

Let's examine the script showing the principle of this selection method ch3/ demo_ selection_proportional.py:

Import part

```
import random
import pandas as pd
import matplotlib.pyplot as plt
from ch3.individual import Individual
```

Proportional selection

```
random.seed(4)
POPULATION_SIZE = 5

unsorted_population = Individual.create_random_population(POPULATION_
SIZE)
population = sorted(unsorted_population, key = lambda ind: ind.fitness,
reverse = True)
fitness_sum = sum([ind.fitness for ind in population])
fitness_map = {}
for i in population:
    i_prob = round(100 * i.fitness / fitness_sum)
    i_label = f'{i.name} | fitness: {i.fitness}, prob: {i_prob}%'
    fitness_map[i_label] = i.fitness
```

Visualization

```
index = ['Sectors']
df = pd.DataFrame(fitness_map, index = index)
df.plot.barh(stacked = True)
for _ in range(POPULATION_SIZE):
    plt.axvline(x = random.random() * fitness_sum, linewidth = 5, color =
'black')
plt.tick_params(axis = 'x', which = 'both', bottom = False, top = False,
```

```
labelbottom = False)
plt.show()
```

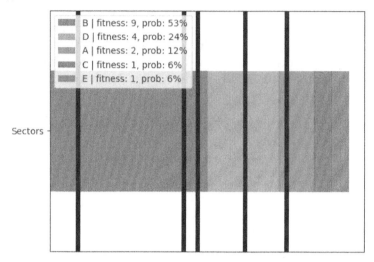

Figure 3.3: *Visualization of Proportional Selection*

Consider the preceding example, as shown in *figure 3.3*, where individual B has a fitness score of 9. The total number of fitness scores is 17, the sector of individual B occupies $9/17 = 0.5294$, that is, 53% of the entire roulette strip. The lengths of sectors for other individuals are calculated in the same way. Black bars are the result of one roulette spin. As a result, we have the following selection result: B, B, B, D, A

The proportional selection can be implemented in the following way ch3/ selection_proportional.py:

```
import random
def selection_proportional(individuals):
    sorted_individuals = sorted(individuals, key = lambda ind: ind.
fitness, reverse = True)
    fitness_sum = sum([ind.fitness for ind in individuals])
    selected = []

    for _ in range(len(sorted_individuals)):
        shave = random.random() * fitness_sum
        roulette_sum = 0
        for ind in sorted_individuals:
            roulette_sum += ind.fitness
            if roulette_sum > shave:
```

```
        selected.append(ind)
        break

    return selected
```

Let's see this selection method in action ch3/example_selection_proportional.
py:

```
import random
from ch3.selection_proportional import selection_proportional
from ch3.individual import Individual

POPULATION_SIZE = 5
random.seed(4)

population = Individual.create_random_population(POPULATION_SIZE)
selected = selection_proportional(population)

print(f"Population: {population}")
print(f"Selected: {selected}")
```

Result

```
Population: [A: 3, B: 4, C: 1, D: 6, E: 7]
Selected: [E: 7, E: 7, D: 6, A: 3, B: 4]
```

Proportional selection method has the possibility to select the worst individual, and also has the possibility to not select best individual.

3.3 Stochastic universal sampling selection

Stochastic universal sampling selection method is an alternative method of proportional selection. In this method, the entire roulette wheel is divided into N cutoffs with equal spacing.

This method smooths out the elements of randomness which proportional selection has, and ensures that the individuals are selected according to the following principle – many good individuals, some average individuals, and a few bad individuals.

It can be demonstrated as follows

ch3/demo_selection_stochastic_universal_sampling.py:

Import part

```
import random
import pandas as pd
import matplotlib.pyplot as plt
```

```
from ch3.individual import Individual
```

Selection

```
POPULATION_SIZE = 5
random.seed(9)

unsorted_population = Individual.create_random_population(POPULATION_
SIZE)
population = sorted(unsorted_population, key = lambda ind: ind.fitness,
reverse = True)

fitness_sum = sum([ind.fitness for ind in population])
fitness_map = {}
for i in population:
    i_prob = round(100 * i.fitness / fitness_sum)
    i_label = f'{i.name} | fitness: {i.fitness}, prob: {i_prob}%'
    fitness_map[i_label] = i.fitness
```

Visualization

```
index = ['Sectors']
df = pd.DataFrame(fitness_map, index = index)
df.plot.barh(stacked = True)
distance = fitness_sum / POPULATION_SIZE
shift = random.random() * distance
for i in range(POPULATION_SIZE):
    plt.axvline(x = shift + distance * i, linewidth = 5, color =
'black')
plt.tick_params(axis = 'x', which = 'both', bottom = False, top = False,
labelbottom = False)
plt.show()
```

Let's take a look at the following *figure 3.4* for the visualization of Stochastic universal sampling selection:

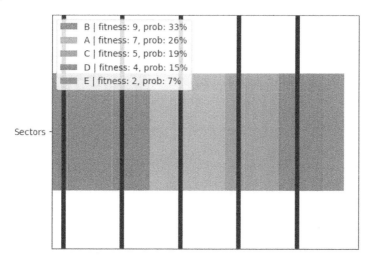

B | fitness: 9, prob: 33%
A | fitness: 7, prob: 26%
C | fitness: 5, prob: 19%
D | fitness: 4, prob: 15%
E | fitness: 2, prob: 7%

Sectors

Figure 3.4: *Visualization of Stochastic Universal Sampling Selection*

The stochastic universal sampling selection can be implemented in the following way ch3/selection_stochastic_universal_sampling.py:

```python
import random

def selection_stochastic_universal_sampling(individuals):
    sorted_individuals = sorted(individuals, key = lambda ind: ind.
fitness, reverse = True)
    fitness_sum = sum([ind.fitness for ind in individuals])

    distance = fitness_sum / len(individuals)
    shift = random.uniform(0, distance)
    borders = [shift + i * distance for i in range(len(individuals))]

    selected = []
    for border in borders:
        i = 0
        roulette_sum = sorted_individuals[i].fitness
        while roulette_sum < border:
            i += 1
            roulette_sum += sorted_individuals[i].fitness
        selected.append(sorted_individuals[i])
    return selected
```

Let's see the stochastic universal sampling selection method in action `example_selection_stochastic_universal_sampling.py`:

```python
import random

from ch3.selection_stochastic_universal_sampling import selection_stochastic_universal_sampling
from ch3.individual import Individual

POPULATION_SIZE = 5
random.seed(1)

population = Individual.create_random_population(POPULATION_SIZE)
selected = selection_stochastic_universal_sampling(population)

print(f"Population: {population}")
print(f"Selected: {selected}")
```

Result

```
Population: [A: 2, B: 9, C: 1, D: 4, E: 1]
Selected: [B: 9, B: 9, B: 9, D: 4, C: 1]
```

> **NOTE: As with the proportional selection method, the stochastic universal sampling selection has the possibility to select the worst individual, and also has the possibility to not select the best individual. Even if it seems contradictory, this approach shows very good results for a particular class of problems.**

3.4 Rank selection

Rank selection has the same principle as proportional selection, but individuals of the population are ranked according to the values of their fitness function. This can be thought of as a sorted list of individuals, ordered from the fittest to the least fit, in which each individual is assigned a number that determines its place in the list, called rank. Rank selection smoothens out the large difference between individuals with high fitness values and individuals with low fitness values.

Let's compare proportion selection with rank selection `ch3/ demo_selection_rank.py`:

Import part

```python
import random

import pandas as pd

import matplotlib.pyplot as plt
```

```
from ch3.individual import Individual
```

Rank selection

```
POPULATION_SIZE = 5
random.seed(2)

unsorted_population = Individual.create_random_population(POPULATION_
SIZE)
population = sorted(unsorted_population, key = lambda ind: ind.fitness,
reverse = True)

fitness_sum = sum([ind.fitness for ind in population])
fitness_map = {}
for i in population:
    i_prob = round(100 * i.fitness / fitness_sum)
    i_label = f'{i.name} | fitness: {i.fitness}, prob: {i_prob}%'
    fitness_map[i_label] = i.fitness

proportional_df = pd.DataFrame(fitness_map, index = ['Sectors'])
proportional_df.plot.barh(stacked = True)
plt.tick_params(axis = 'x', which = 'both', bottom = False, top = False,
labelbottom = False)
plt.title('Fitness Proportional Sectors')
plt.show()

rank_step = 1 / POPULATION_SIZE
rank_sum = sum([1 - rank_step * i for i in range(len(population))])
rank_map = {}

for i in range(len(population)):
    i_rank = i + 1
    i_rank_proportion = 1 - i * rank_step
    i_prob = round(100 * i_rank_proportion / rank_sum)
    i_label = f'{population[i].name} | rank: {i_rank}, prob: {i_prob}%'
    rank_map[i_label] = i_rank_proportion
```

Visualization

```
rank_df = pd.DataFrame(rank_map, index = ['Sectors'])
rank_df.plot.barh(stacked = True)
plt.tick_params(axis = 'x', which = 'both', bottom = False, top = False,
labelbottom = False)
```

```
plt.title('Rank Proportional Sectors')
plt.show()
```

We already saw that proportional selection uses the roulette sectors, as shown in the following *figure 3.5:*

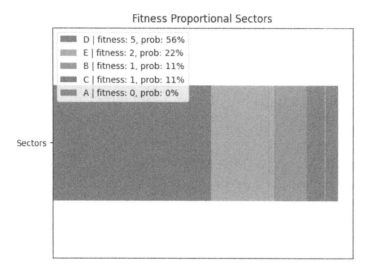

Figure 3.5: Fitness Proportional Sectors

But for the same population, rank selection will use the following roulette (as shown in the following *figure 3.6*):

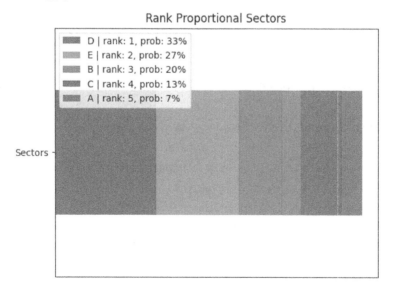

Figure 3.6: Rank Sectors

We see that the best individual in rank selection has a lower chance of being selected than it has in the proportional selection, and on the contrary, the worst individual, which had no chance of being selected in proportional selection has some positive probability of being selected.

How rank selection is calculated?

rank_shift := 1 / population_size = 1 / 5 = 0.2

rank_weight_sum := (population_size + 1) / 2 = 3

*Nth_individual_weight := (1 – (rank - 1) x rank_shift) / rank_weight_sum * 100%*

For D we have (1 – (0 x 0.2)) / 3 * 100% = 33%

For E we have (1 – (1 x 0.2)) / 3 * 100% = 27%

For B we have (1 – (2 x 0.2)) / 3 * 100% = 20%

And so on.

Rank selection implementation ch3/selection_rank.py:

```python
import random

def selection_rank(individuals):
    sorted_individuals = sorted(individuals, key = lambda ind: ind.
fitness, reverse = True)
    rank_distance = 1 / len(individuals)
    ranks = [(1 - i * rank_distance) for i in range(len(individuals))]
    ranks_sum = sum(ranks)
    selected = []

    for _ in range(len(sorted_individuals)):
        shave = random.random() * ranks_sum
        rank_sum = 0
        for i in range(len(sorted_individuals)):
            rank_sum += ranks[i]
            if rank_sum > shave:
                selected.append(sorted_individuals[i])
                break

    return selected
```

Let's examine how rank selection works ch3/example_selection_rank.py:

```python
import random

from ch3.selection_rank import selection_rank
```

```
from ch3.individual import Individual

POPULATION_SIZE = 5
random.seed(18)

population = Individual.create_random_population(POPULATION_SIZE)
selected = selection_rank(population)

print(f'Population: {population}')
print(f'Selected: {selected}')
```

Result

```
Population: [A: 2, B: 1, C: 10, D: 7, E: 5]
Selected: [C: 10, B: 1, E: 5, C: 10, C: 10]
```

3.5 Elite selection

As we have already seen, none of the selection methods that we have considered – tournament, proportional, stochastic universal sampling, and rank selection – guarantee the selection of the best individual. The genes of the best individual can be very valuable for the next generations, so there is an approach that protects the best individuals. This method is called **elite selection**. Elite selection can be based on another method, such as rank selection, but the main change in this method is the guaranteed inclusion of the best individuals in the selected population.

Elite selection implementation ch3/`selection_rank_with_elite.py`:

```
import random

def selection_rank_with_elite(individuals, elite_size = 0):
    sorted_individuals = sorted(individuals, key = lambda ind: ind.
fitness, reverse = True)
    rank_distance = 1 / len(individuals)
    ranks = [(1 - i * rank_distance) for i in range(len(individuals))]
    ranks_sum = sum(ranks)
    selected = sorted_individuals[0:elite_size]

    for i in range(len(sorted_individuals) - elite_size):
        shave = random.random() * ranks_sum
        rank_sum = 0
        for i in range(len(sorted_individuals)):
            rank_sum += ranks[i]
```

```
    if rank_sum > shave:
        selected.append(sorted_individuals[i])
        break

return selected
```

Let's see this method in action ch3/example_selection_rank_with_elite.py:

```
import random

from ch3.selection_rank_with_elite import selection_rank_with_elite
from ch3.individual import Individual

POPULATION_SIZE = 5
random.seed(3)

population = Individual.create_random_population(POPULATION_SIZE)
selected = selection_rank_with_elite(population, elite_size = 2)

print(f"Population: {population}")
print(f"Population: {selected}")
```

Result

```
Population: [A: 3, B: 9, C: 8, D: 2, E: 5]
Population: [B: 9, C: 8, A: 3, C: 8, C: 8]
```

As we see B and C are the two best individuals in population, they form the elite and are being selected by default.

> **NOTE: Elite selection is a handy method of selection in conditions where an individual's fitness may degenerate as a result of crossover or mutation. We need to protect the best individuals, and try to spread their genes among the population.**

Conclusion

Selection is a very important part of the evolution process; every individual aims to generate an offspring. The selection process is random by nature. We have studied several selection methods, each of which has its pros and cons. You can use one of these methods or any modification.

In the next chapter, we will study the next part of evolution called crossover.

Points to remember

- Each selection method has the following principle -- adapted individuals have a higher possibility to be selected than the abandoned ones.

- Even abandoned individuals can have something valuable in their genes, so we have to leave a positive probability for them to be selected.

Multiple choice questions

1. **Which selection method guarantees that the best individual will be selected?**

    a) Rank selection

    b) Elite selection

    c) Tournament selection

    d) Proportional selection

2. **Which selection method guarantees that the worst individual will not be selected?**

    a) Rank selection

    b) Elite selection

    c) Tournament selection

    d) Proportional selection

3. **Say we have the following population: A: 3, B: 9, C: 8, D: 2, E: 5. And we have selected population: B: 9, C: 8, A: 3, C: 8, C: 8. What selection method have we used?**

    a) Elite selection

    b) Proportional selection

    c) It's impossible to answer this question, it can be any of selection methods

Answers

1. b
2. c
3. c

Key terms

- **Tournament selection:** The selection based on choosing the best individual in a subgroup.
- **Proportional selection:** It is a method of selecting individuals, in which each individual is assigned a probability proportional to the values of their fitness functions.
- **Rank selection:** It is a method of selecting individuals, in which each individual is assigned a probability ranked according to the values of their fitness function.
- **Elite selection:** The selection strategy protecting the best individuals.

CHAPTER 4
Crossover

Crossover is the process of forming new individuals from existing individuals while maintaining traits. The main purpose of crossing is the exchange of experience. This approach greatly speeds up finding an acceptable solution. Crossover is the next logical action that occurs after selection.

Structure

In this chapter, we will look at the following crossover methods:

- One-point crossover
- N-point crossover
- Uniform crossover
- Linear combination crossover
- Blend crossover
- Order crossover
- Fitness driven crossover

Objectives

- Understand what crossover is
- Introduce main crossover methods

• Get visualization and implementation of each method

4.1 One-point crossover

In one-point crossover, a point in a gene sequence is randomly selected by dividing the gene sequence into two parts. New individuals are created by crossing these two parts. Please take a look at the following *figure 4.1:*

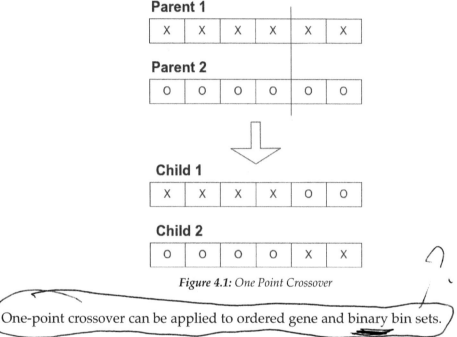

Figure 4.1: One Point Crossover

One-point crossover can be applied to ordered gene and binary bin sets.

If the gene sequence consists of one element, then a simple exchange of genes between the parents happens, and each of the children is a clone of one of the parents. Please take a look at the following *figure 4.2:*

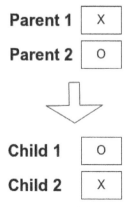

Figure 4.2: One-point Crossover for 1-element gene sequence

If the gene sequence consists of two elements, then the genes are exchanged in a crisscross way. Please take a look at the following *figure 4.3*:

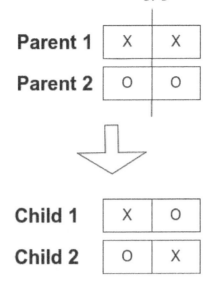

Figure 4.3: One-point Crossover for 2-element gene sequence

Here we will show an implementation of one-point crossover to an ordered gene set ch4/one_point.py:

Import part

```
import copy
import random
```

One-point crossover

```
def crossover_one_point(p1, p2):
    point = random.randint(1, len(p1) - 1)
    c1, c2 = copy.deepcopy(p1), copy.deepcopy(p2)
    c1[point:], c2[point:] = p2[point:], p1[point:]
    return [c1, c2]
```

Example

```
random.seed(2)

p1 = [random.randint(0, 9) for _ in range(5)]
p2 = [random.randint(0, 9) for _ in range(5)]

offspring = crossover_one_point(p1, p2)
```

```
print(f'Parent 1: {p1}')
print(f'Parent 2: {p2}')
print(f'Child 1: {offspring[0]}')
print(f'Child 2: {offspring[1]}')
```

Result

Parent 1	0	1	1	5	2
Parent 2	4	4	9	3	9
Child 1	0	4	9	3	9
Child 2	4	1	1	5	2

4.2 N-point crossover

N-point crossover is a logical continuation of one-point crossover, but instead of choosing only one point in a gene sequence, N points are selected, and genes are being exchanged in a crisscross way. Please take a look at the following *figure 4.4*:

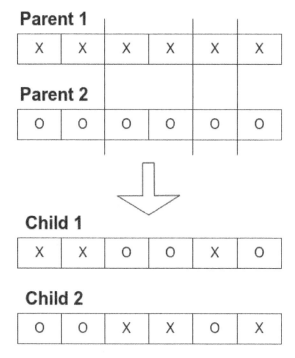

Figure 4.4: N-Point Crossover

Let's see an implementation of N-point crossover that is applied to an ordered gene set ch4/n_point.py:

Import part

```
import copy
import random
```

N-point crossover

```
def crossover_n_point(p1, p2, n):
    ps = random.sample(range(1, len(p1) - 1), n)
    ps.append(0)
    ps.append(len(p1))
    ps = sorted(ps)
    c1, c2 = copy.deepcopy(p1), copy.deepcopy(p2)
    for i in range(0, n + 1):
        if i % 2 == 0:
            continue
        c1[ps[i]:ps[i + 1]] = p2[ps[i]:ps[i + 1]]
        c2[ps[i]:ps[i + 1]] = p1[ps[i]:ps[i + 1]]
    return [c1, c2]
```

Example

```
random.seed(3)

p1 = [random.randint(0, 9) for _ in range(6)]
p2 = [random.randint(10, 19) for _ in range(6)]

offspring = crossover_n_point(p1, p2, 3)

print(f'Parent 1: {p1}')
print(f'Parent 2: {p2}')
print(f'Child 1: {offspring[0]}')
print(f'Child 2: {offspring[1]}')
```

Result

Parent 1	3	9	8	2	5	9
Parent 2	17	19	11	19	10	17
Child 1	3	19	11	2	10	17
Child 2	17	9	8	19	5	9

4.3 Uniform crossover

Uniform crossover randomly selects some points in the parent's gene chain, and swaps the genes at these points. Please take a look at the following *figure 4.5:*

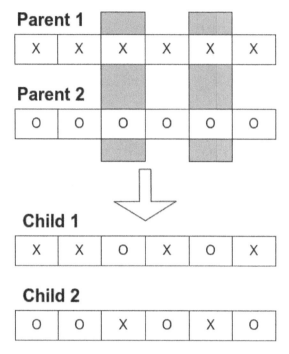

Figure 4.5: *Uniform Crossover*

Implementation of uniform crossover `ch4/uniform.py`:

Import part

```
import copy
import random
```

Uniform crossover

```python
def crossover_uniform(p1, p2, prop):
    c1 = copy.deepcopy(p1)
    c2 = copy.deepcopy(p2)

    for i in range(len(p1)):
        if random.random() < prop:
            c1[i], c2[i] = p2[i], p1[i]

    return [c1, c2]
```

Example

```
random.seed(3)

p1 = [random.randint(0, 9) for _ in range(6)]
p2 = [random.randint(10, 19) for _ in range(6)]

offspring = crossover_uniform(p1, p2, 0.5)

print(f'Parent 1: {p1}')
print(f'Parent 2: {p2}')
print(f'Child 1: {offspring[0]}')
print(f'Child 2: {offspring[1]}')
```

Result

Parent 1	3	9	8	2	5	9
Parent 2	17	19	11	19	10	17
Child 1	17	19	8	19	5	17
Child 2	3	9	11	2	10	9

4.4 Linear combination crossover

Linear combination crossover is the example of a crossover without any randomness. Child genes is a simple linear combination of parent genes:

($x1 + \alpha |x2 - x1|$, $x2 - \alpha |x2 - x1|$), where α is the parameter of linear combination in range [0, 1].

> NOTE: If α equals 0 or 1, then children are the same as parents.
>
> If α equals 0.5, then we have twins in offspring (both children are the same).
>
> If we want only new individuals to be created, then we can restrict α to this range (0, 0.5).

Let's take a look at the following *figure 4.6:*

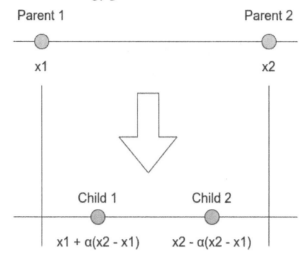

Figure 4.6: *Linear Combination Crossover*

Implementation of linear crossover is just arithmetic operation applied to real gene set ch4/linear.py:

Import part

```
import copy
import random
```

Linear crossover

```
def crossover_linear(p1, p2, alpha):
    c1 = copy.deepcopy(p1)
    c2 = copy.deepcopy(p2)

    for i in range(len(p1)):
        c1[i] = round(p1[i] + alpha * (p2[i] - p1[i]), 2)
        c2[i] = round(p2[i] - alpha * (p2[i] - p1[i]), 2)

    return [c1, c2]
```

Example

```
random.seed(3)

p1 = [round(random.uniform(0, 10), 2) for _ in range(6)]
p2 = [round(random.uniform(0, 10), 2) for _ in range(6)]
```

```
offspring = crossover_linear(p1, p2, 0.3)

print(f'Parent 1: {p1}')
print(f'Parent 2: {p2}')
print(f'Child 1: {offspring[0]}')
print(f'Child 2: {offspring[1]}')
```

Result

Parent 1	2.38	5.44	3.7	6.04	6.26	0.66
Parent 2	0.13	8.37	2.59	2.34	9.96	4.7
Child 1	1.71	6.32	3.37	4.93	7.37	1.87
Child 2	0.8	7.49	2.92	3.45	8.85	3.49

4.5 Blend crossover

Blend crossover method chooses random genes in the range defined by parent genes. The range for children genes is defined as follows:

[x1 - α(x2 - x1) , x2 + α(x2 - x1)], where α is the parameter that expands the parent genes range. Please take a look at the following *figure 4.7:*

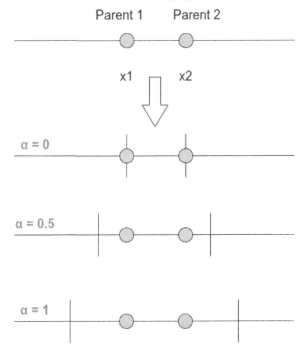

Figure 4.7: *α parameter influence*

Usually, $\alpha = 0.5$. Please take a look at the following *figure 4.8*:

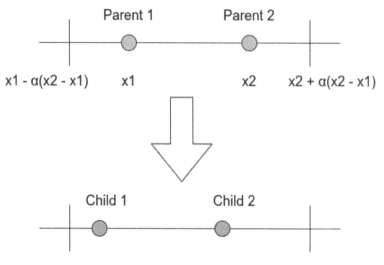

Figure 4.8: Blend crossover

Like linear crossover, blend crossover is applied to a real gene set; let's study an implementation ch4/blend.py:

Import part

```
import copy
import random
```

Blend crossover

```
def crossover_blend(p1, p2, alpha):
    c1 = copy.deepcopy(p1)
    c2 = copy.deepcopy(p2)

    for i in range(len(p1)):
        l = min(c1[i], c2[i]) - alpha * abs(c2[i] - c1[i])
        u = max(c1[i], c2[i]) + alpha * abs(c2[i] - c1[i])
        c1[i] = round(l + random.random() * (u - l), 2)
        c2[i] = round(l + random.random() * (u - l), 2)

    return [c1, c2]
```

Example

```
random.seed(3)
p1 = [round(random.uniform(0, 10), 2) for _ in range(6)]
```

```
p2 = [round(random.uniform(0, 10), 2) for _ in range(6)]

offspring = crossover_blend(p1, p2, 0.5)

print(f'Parent 1: {p1}')
print(f'Parent 2: {p2}')
print(f'Child 1: {offspring[0]}')
print(f'Child 2: {offspring[1]}')
```

Result

Parent 1	2.38	5.44	3.7	6.04	6.26	0.66
Parent 2	0.13	8.37	2.59	2.34	9.96	4.7
Child 1	2.77	7.72	3.44	4.36	9.38	4.77
Child 2	1.15	4.86	3.96	5.98	4.88	3.42

4.6 Order crossover

Order crossover is used for ordered genes; the main principle in this approach is to preserve the order of parent genes. We will show how this method works with an example:

Say, we have two individuals with ordered genes:

Parent 1: (1, 7, 4, 5, 9, 2, 8, 3, 6)

Parent 2: (3, 1, 5, 4, 9, 8, 6, 2, 7)

We choose a random range in genes chain and swap it. Please take a look at the following *figure 4.9:*

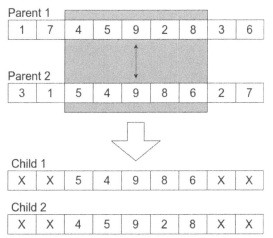

Figure 4.9: *Order Crossover. Parent genes swap*

Now, we will try to find the next number in **Parent 1**, which wasn't mentioned in **Child 1** yet:

Parent 1: (1, 7, 4, 5, 9, 2, 8 -> 3, 6) – the next number is 3.

Child 1: (X, X, 5, 4, 9, 8, 6, X, X) – doesn't contain 3 yet.

Please take a look at the following *figure 4.10:*

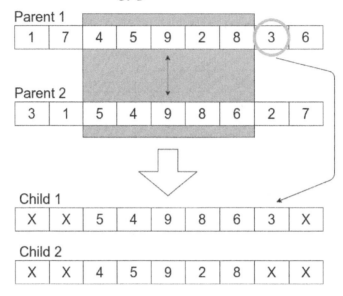

Figure 4.10: Order Crossover. Child 1 Filling – step 1.

The same happens for **Child 2**; in **Parent 2** the next number is 2, but it is already mentioned in **Child 2** – then we take the next one:

Parent 2: (3, 1, 5, 4, 9, 8, 6 -> 2, 7) – the next number is 2.

Child 2: (X, X, 4, 5, 9, 2, 8, X, X) – already contains 2.

Checking the next number:

Parent 2: (3, 1, 5, 4, 9, 8, 6, 2 -> 7) – the next number is 7.

Child 2: (X, X, 4, 5, 9, 2, 8, X, X) – doesn't contain 7 yet.

Please take a look at the following *figure 4.11:*

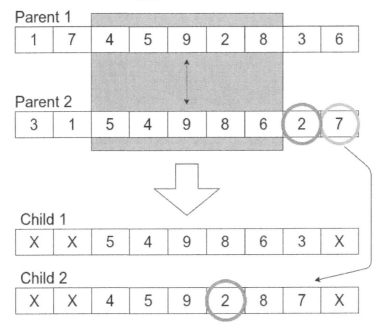

Figure 4.11: Order Crossover. Child 2 Filling – step 1.

Keep going for **Child 1;** the next **Parent 1** number is 6 and this number is mentioned in **Child 1** too, so we're taking the next one:

Parent 1: (1, 7, 4, 5, 9, 2, 8, 3 -> 6) – the next number is 6.

Child 1: (X, X, 5, 4, 9, 8, 6, 3, X) – already contains 3.

Checking the next number:

Parent 1: (-> 1, 7, 4, 5, 9, 2, 8, 3, 6) – the next number is 1.

Child 1: (X, X, 5, 4, 9, 8, 6, 3, X) – doesn't contain 1 yet.

Please take a look at the following *figure 4.12:*

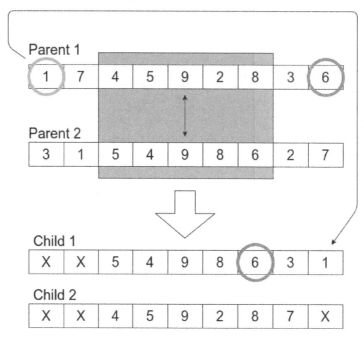

Figure 4.12: *Order Crossover. Child 1 Filling – step 2.*

We hope you have got the principle. As a result, we will have the following offspring. Please take a look at the following *figure 4.13:*

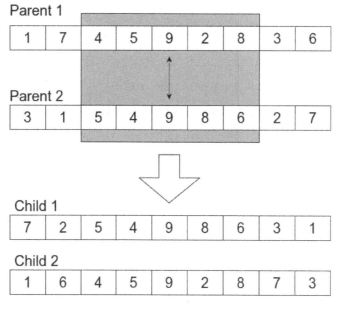

Figure 4.13: *Order Crossover. Result*

In very high dimension tasks with a large number of variables, an execution of order crossover can be rather time-consuming; you have to pay attention to this fact by applying this method. Implementation of order crossover ch4/order.py:

Import part

```
import random
from math import nan
```

Order crossover

```
def crossover_order(p1, p2):
    zero_shift = min(p1)
    length = len(p1)
    start, end = sorted([random.randrange(length) for _ in range(2)])
    c1, c2 = [nan] * length, [nan] * length
    t1, t2 = [x - zero_shift for x in p1], [x - zero_shift for x in p2]

    spaces1, spaces2 = [True] * length, [True] * length
    for i in range(length):
        if i < start or i > end:
            spaces1[t2[i]] = False
            spaces2[t1[i]] = False

    j1, j2 = end + 1, end + 1
    for i in range(length):
        if not spaces1[t1[(end + i + 1) % length]]:
            c1[j1 % length] = t1[(end + i + 1) % length]
            j1 += 1

        if not spaces2[t2[(i + end + 1) % length]]:
            c2[j2 % length] = t2[(i + end + 1) % length]
            j2 += 1

    for i in range(start, end + 1):
        c1[i], c2[i] = t2[i], t1[i]
    return [[x + zero_shift for x in c1], [x + zero_shift for x in c2]]
```

Example

```
random.seed(10)

p1 = random.sample(range(1, 10), 9)
```

```
p2 = random.sample(range(1, 10), 9)
offspring = crossover_order(p1, p2)

print(f'Parent 1: {p1}')
print(f'Parent 2: {p2}')
print(f'Child 1: {offspring[0]}')
print(f'Child 2: {offspring[1]}')
```

Result

Parent 1	1	7	4	5	9	2	8	3	6
Parent 2	3	1	5	4	9	8	6	2	7
Child 1	7	2	5	4	9	8	6	3	1
Child 2	1	6	4	5	9	2	8	7	3

4.7 Fitness driven crossover

Fitness driven crossover is an approach that compares the child to the parent and selects the best one. The main principle of this approach is that children should be better than their parents or not at all.

In some tasks, the crossing operation is very unpredictable, and carries a high risk of destroying the accumulated positive experience. Then, as soon as the individuals appear to begin to adapt well to the environment, their genotype can be destroyed after crossing, and as a result, their unique genetic adaptation will be destroyed. Please take a look at the following *figure 4.14:*

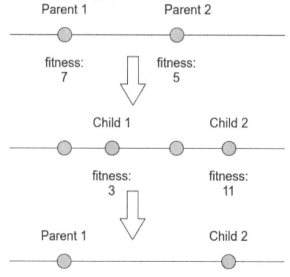

Figure 4.14: Order Crossover. Result

NOTE: You can notice that fitness driven crossover shares the same principle as elite selection which we covered in *Chapter 3: Selection* – not to lose valuable individuals.

And a reasonable question could be: Why not always do this? Why don't we protect the best ones all the time?

Sometimes it makes sense, but evolution is very tricky and unpredictable thing; sometimes it can make one step back and two steps forward. Tiny mammals from the Jurassic period lived on the brink of survival, but after millions of years, this species led to the appearance of human.

We will get back to this question in further chapters.

Fitness driven crossover can be based on any other crossover method. For example, let's examine the implementation of fitness driven crossover based on blend crossover ch4/fitness_driven.py:

Import part

```
import copy

import random

from math import sin, cos
```

Individual

```
def fitness_function(x, y):
    return sin(x) * cos(y)


class Individual:

    def __init__(self, x, y) -> None:
        self.gene_set = [x, y]
        self.fitness = fitness_function(x, y)

    def __str__(self):
        return f'x: {self.gene_set[0]}, '\
               f'y: {self.gene_set[1]}, '\
               f'fitness: {round(self.fitness, 4)}'


def generate_random():
    return Individual(round(random.random(), 2), round(random.random(),
2))
```

Fitness driven blend crossover

```python
def crossover_fitness_driven_blend(ind1, ind2, alpha):
    c1 = copy.deepcopy(ind1.gene_set)
    c2 = copy.deepcopy(ind2.gene_set)

    for i in range(len(c1)):
        l = min(c1[i], c2[i]) - alpha * abs(c2[i] - c1[i])
        u = max(c1[i], c2[i]) + alpha * abs(c2[i] - c1[i])
        c1[i] = round(l + random.random() * (u - l), 2)
        c2[i] = round(l + random.random() * (u - l), 2)

    child1 = Individual(c1[0], c1[1])
    child2 = Individual(c1[0], c1[1])

    candidates = [ind1, ind2, child1, child2]

    best = sorted(candidates, key = lambda ind: ind.fitness, reverse = True)

    return best[0:2]
```

Example

```python
random.seed(3)

p1, p2 = generate_random(), generate_random()

offspring = crossover_fitness_driven_blend(p1, p2, 0.5)

print(f'Parent 1: {p1}')
print(f'Parent 2: {p2}')

print(f'Child 1: {offspring[0]}')
print(f'Child 2: {offspring[1]}')
```

Result

Parent 1 fitness: 0.2039	0.24	0.54
Parent 2 fitness: 0.2985	0.37	0.6
Child 1 fitness: 0.2985	0.37	0.6
Child 2 fitness: 0.291	0.34	0.51

We see that **Child 1** is the copy of **Parent 2**.

Conclusion

Crossover is a very specific evolutionary method. While the selection is an objective factor that is determined by nature and environment, the crossover mechanisms for each species can be very different. There are insect species that may not use crossbreeding as such! So, in genetic algorithms, crossover methods are chosen only as the source of the problem to be solved, and it is impossible to decide in advance which method is better. An incorrectly chosen crossover method can stop the evolutionary improvement of a population, and therefore make the search for a solution ineffective.

In the next chapter, we will study the last part of evolution called mutation.

Points to remember

- **Each crossover method has the principle:** Try to change the experience of individuals, but not to make soup of the genes, destroying the whole gene structure.

- There is no predetermined list of crossover methods. You can implement your own crossover method for specific task.

Multiple choice questions

1. **We have a population of individuals with genes: (x,y) where x and y lie in range (-10, 10). We use blend crossover with $\alpha = 0$ in our genetic algorithm flow (without mutation). What can we say about our population after 50 generations?**

   a) All individuals will be concentrated near one point because the best solution will be found.

   b) All individuals will be uniformly distributed in square (-10,10) X (-10,10).

   c) All individuals will be concentrated near one point because blend crossover with $\alpha = 0$ doesn't expand the range of genes and all children genes will be shrinking.

2. **We have a population of individuals with ordered genes: (1 2,...,9). Our gene structure is very fragile and there is a high probability that after each crossover, new offspring will be worse than their parents. What approach can we use to solve that issue?**

   a) Order Crossover

   b) Fitness Driven Crossover based on Order Crossover

    c)   One Point Crossover

    d)   Fitness Driven Crossover based on Uniform Crossover

Answers

1. c
2. b

Questions

1. Why the usage of blend crossover with very high α can lead to poor results of genetic algorithm execution?

2. Say we have a real gene set for genetic algorithm finding maxima of multivariable function f(x,y,z). Can we get acceptable results with the usage of order crossover here?

Key terms

- **One Point crossover:** Exchange of gene "tails".

- **N-Point crossover:** Crisscross gene exchange.

- **Uniform crossover:** Random gene swap.

- **Blending crossover:** Random gene in range determined by parent genes.

- **Order crossover:** Preserving parent genes order .

- **Fitness driven crossover:** Choosing best between children and parents.

CHAPTER 5
Mutation

A mutation is a random change in genes with the aim of improving an individual's ability to survive. A mutation has no direction; it is a simple attempt at introducing a new feature that will give the future individual additional advantages. If you look at the history of evolution, it might seem that all mutations of species were strictly directed, and were extremely successful. But this is not right. An unsuccessful mutation makes an individual less viable due to which it cannot leave offspring, and therefore pass on its genes. Consequently, individuals and species with unsuccessful mutations do not exist for a long time, which means they do not leave a significant trace in the evolutionary chain.

The mechanism of mutations is the driving force of evolution; it helps species to improve, as well as to adapt to environmental conditions.

Structure

The mechanisms of mutation are simpler than the mechanisms of selection and crossing. In this chapter, we will look at the following main ones:

- Random deviation mutation
- Exchange mutation
- Shift mutation
- Bit flip mutation

- Inversion mutation
- Shuffle mutation
- Fitness driven mutation

Objectives

- Understand basic principles of mutation
- Introduce main mutation methods

5.1 Random deviation mutation

Random deviation mutation is mainly applied to a real set of genes. A random variable is added to the gene with a certain probability, usually with an average of 0. Refer to the following *figure 5.1:*

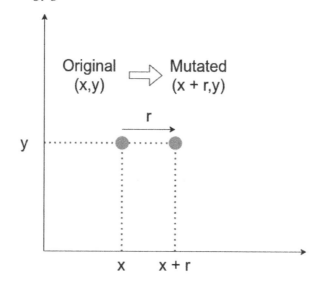

Figure 5.1: *Random Deviation mutation*

Random deviation mutation can be implemented by adding the random variable with normal distribution (average = 0 and sigma = 1) ch5/random_deviation.py:

Random deviation mutation

```
def mutation_random_deviation(ind, mu, sigma, p):
    mut = copy.deepcopy(ind)
    for i in range(len(mut)):
        if random.random() < p:
```

```
            mut[i] = mut[i] + random.gauss(mu, sigma)
    return mut
```

Example

```
random.seed(0)


ind = [random.uniform(0, 10) for _ in range(2)]
mut = mutation_random_deviation(ind, 0, 1, 0.3)


print(f'Original: {ind}')
print(f'Mutated: {mut}')
```

Result

Original	8.44	7.57
Mutated	8.44	6.56

5.2 Exchange mutation

Mutation exchange is mainly applied to a binary or ordered set of genes. A pair of genes are exchanged from randomly selected positions. Please refer to the following *figure 5.2*:

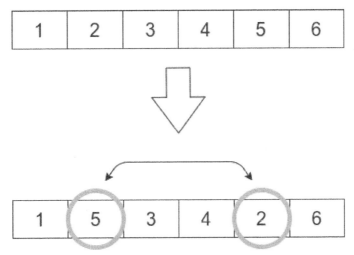

Figure 5.2: Exchange mutation

In concrete implementation, we pick two random indices in the list of genes, and change its values ch5/exchange.py:

Exchange mutation

```
def mutation_exchange(ind):
    mut = copy.deepcopy(ind)
    pos = random.sample(range(0, len(mut)), 2)
    g1 = mut[pos[0]]
    g2 = mut[pos[1]]
    mut[pos[1]] = g1
    mut[pos[0]] = g2
    return mut
```

Example

```
random.seed(1)

ind = list(range(1, 7))
mut = mutation_exchange(ind)

print(f'Original: {ind}')
print(f'Mutated: {mut}')
```

Result

Original	1	2	3	4	5	6
Mutated	1	5	3	4	2	6

5.3 Shift mutation

Shift Mutation is moving a gene from a randomly selected position by a random number of positions to the left or right. The content of all intermediate genes is shifted by one position. This mutation method is applied to a binary or ordered set of genes. Refer to the following *figure 5.3*:

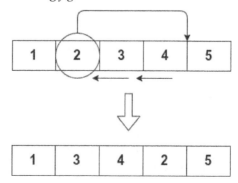

Figure 5.3: *Shift Mutation*

There are three different approaches of shift mutation implementation:

- **Bounded shifting:** This approach allows to shift gene without crossing gene list borders, that is, last element cannot shift to first, and vice versa. In list [1,2,3,4,5] we can pick gene 3, and put it to position with index 0, and get the result [3,1,2,4,5].

- **Unbounded shifting:** This approach allows to shift gene with crossing gene list borders. For example, in list [1,2,3,4,5], we can pick gene 3 and put it to position with index 0 and get the result [3,2,4,5,1].

Following is an example of implementation of shift mutation `ch5/shift.py`:

Import part

```
import copy
import random
from math import copysign
```

Shift mutation (bounded shifting approach)

```
def mutation_shift(ind):
    mut = copy.deepcopy(ind)
    pos = random.sample(range(0, len(mut)), 2)
    g1 = mut[pos[0]]
    dir = int(copysign(1, pos[1] - pos[0]))
    for i in range(pos[0], pos[1], dir):
        mut[i] = mut[i + dir]
    mut[pos[1]] = g1
    return mut
```

Example

```
random.seed(21)

ind = list(range(1, 6))
mut = mutation_shift(ind)
print(f'Original: {ind}')
print(f'Mutated: {mut}')
```

Result

Original	1	2	3	4	5
Mutated	1	3	4	2	5

5.4 Bit flip mutation

This type of mutation is applied to the binary gene set. Random gene is selected, and bit flipping is provoked, from 1 to 0 or from 0 to 1. Let's take a look at the following *figure 5.4*:

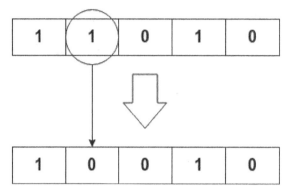

Figure 5.4: *Bit Flip Mutation*

To realize this method, we have to pick a random gene and make an addition of 1 by module 2 ch5/bit_flip.py:

Bit flip mutation

```python
def mutation_bit_flip(ind):
    mut = copy.deepcopy(ind)
    pos = random.randint(0, len(ind) - 1)
    g1 = mut[pos]
    mut[pos] = (g1 + 1) % 2
    return mut
```

Example

```python
random.seed(21)

ind = [random.randint(0, 1) for _ in range(0, 5)]
mut = mutation_bit_flip(ind)

print(f'Original: {ind}')
print(f'Mutated: {mut}')
```

Result

Original	0	1	1	1	1
Mutated	0	0	1	1	1

5.5 Inversion mutation

Inversion mutation picks a random subrange and changes the order of the values in it. This mutation method is applied to a binary or ordered set of genes. Refer to the following *figure 5.5:*

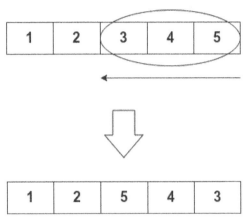

Figure 5.5: *Inversion Mutation*

There are two different approaches of implementation of inversion mutation, which are as follows:

1. **Unbounded subrange:** This approach allows to select through the end subrange, in the list [1,2,3,4,5]; we can pick subrange with indices [3:1] as [4,5,1,2] and get the result [5,4,3,2,1].

2. **Bounded subrange:** This approach doesn't allow to go through the end, which means that the first index of a subrange is always lower than the last index of subrange.

Here is an example implementation of bounded subrange approach ch5/inversion. py:

Inversion mutation

```
def mutation_inversion(ind):
    mut = copy.deepcopy(ind)
    temp = copy.deepcopy(ind)
    pos = sorted(random.sample(range(0, len(mut)), 2))
    for i in range(0, (pos[1] - pos[0]) + 1):
        mut[pos[0] + i] = temp[pos[1] - i]

    return mut
```

Example

```
random.seed(5)

ind = list(range(1, 6))
mut = mutation_inversion(ind)

print(f'Original: {ind}')
print(f'Mutated: {mut}')
```

Result

Original	1	2	3	4	5
Mutated	1	2	5	4	3

5.6 Shuffle mutation

Shuffle mutation, like inversion mutation, picks a random subrange, but instead of changing the order of the values in it, it just shuffles the values. This mutation method is applied to a binary or ordered set of genes. Refer to the following *figure 5.6:*

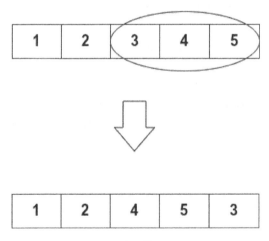

Figure 5.6: Shuffle Mutation

Similar to the inversion mutation, there are two different approaches of implementation of shuffle mutation -- unbounded subrange and bounded subrange.

Here is the example of implementation of shuffle mutation ch5/shuffle.py:

Shuffle mutation

```
def mutation_shuffle(ind):
    mut = copy.deepcopy(ind)
```

```
pos = sorted(random.sample(range(0, len(mut)), 2))
subrange = mut[pos[0]:pos[1] + 1]
random.shuffle(subrange)
mut[pos[0]:pos[1] + 1] = subrange
return mut
```

Example

```
random.seed(13)

ind = list(range(1, 6))
mut = mutation_shuffle(ind)

print(f'Original: {ind}')
print(f'Mutated: {mut}')
```

Result

Original	1	2	3	4	5
Mutated	1	2	4	3	5

5.7 Fitness driven mutation

Fitness driven mutation, like the fitness driven crossover, is an approach that is trying to obtain only positive changes. We run several mutations and pick the best one; if all mutations are worse than the original individual, then we leave the original without a mutation. Refer to the following *figure 5.7*:

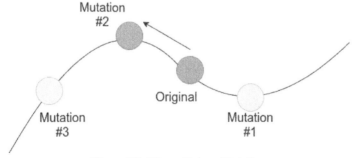

Figure 5.7: Fitness Driven Mutation

NOTE: You have to make only a finite number of mutation tries. It is unacceptable to make an infinite loop trying to find any positive mutation. Because there can be a situation when you're trying to mutate the best individual, and each mutation makes it worse than it is now. Thus, your genetic algorithm will get stuck, trying to improve something that is already perfect.

Following are the two different approaches of implementation of fitness driven mutation:

- **Pick first positive:** This approach generates mutations one by one, and stops when first positive mutation is found. This approach is better in terms of the algorithm speed.
- **Pick best positive:** This approach generates all mutations, then picks the best one. This approach can improve population better but is worse in terms of the algorithm speed.

Fitness driven mutation can be based on any other mutation technique. Here we have the implementation of random deviation picking the first positive fitness driven mutation ch5/random_deviation.py:

Import part

```
import copy
import random
from math import sin
from typing import List
```

Fitness function

```
def func(x):
    return sin(x) - .2 * abs(x)
```

Individual

```
class Individual:

    def __init__(self, gene_list: List[float]) -> None:
        self.gene_list = gene_list
        self.fitness = func(self.gene_list[0])

    def __str__(self):
        return f'x: {self.gene_list[0]}, fitness: {self.fitness}'
```

Fitness driven random deviation mutation (pick first positive approach)

```
def mutation_fitness_driven_random_deviation(ind, mu, sigma, p, max_tries = 3):
    for t in range(0, max_tries):
        mut_genes = copy.deepcopy(ind.gene_list)
        for i in range(len(mut_genes)):
            if random.random() < p:
```

```
                mut_genes[i] = mut_genes[i] + random.gauss(mu, sigma)
        mut = Individual(mut_genes)
        if ind.fitness < mut.fitness:
            return mut
    return ind
```

Example

```
random.seed(14)

ind = Individual([random.uniform(-10, 10)])
mut = mutation_fitness_driven_random_deviation(ind, 0, 1, 3)

print(f'Original: ({ind})')
print(f'Mutated: ({mut})')
```

Result

Original fitness: -2.57	-7.86
Mutated fitness: -1.94	-6.88

Conclusion

Just as in nature, in computational problems, the mutation is usually more important than crossing. Yes, it is possible to construct successive GA algorithm architecture without crossing, but with a mutation. But architecture without mutation is impossible in principle. In the wild, some species reproduce themselves by simple cloning with mutation, and this approach ensures their development and survival.

And so, we ended up with the basic operations performed by the GA. In the next chapter, we will look at how you can compare and evaluate different genetic operations with each other so that you can choose the best architecture of the GA for a specific problem.

Points to remember

- Mutation has to add light changes to individual genes. The mutation which changes genes drastically is very dangerous, and can ruin all positive experience which was accumulated by an individual, and even the whole population.

- There is no predetermined list of mutation methods. You can implement your own mutation method for specific task.

- Mutation is absolutely random process, and there is no guarantee that the mutation will improve an individual.

Multiple choice questions

1. **In population, we have the best individual and this individual is very valuable to us. We want to save it or get an improved version in the next generation. What GA architecture should we choose?**

    a)   Rank selection, uniform crossover, fitness driven mutation

    b)   Elite selection, fitness driven crossover, fitness driven mutation

    c)   Elite selection, one-point crossover, fitness driven mutation

2. **We have the following gene set (0,1,1,0) and fitness function (b1,b2,b3,b4) = b1 + b2 + b3 + b4 , ie fitness(0,1,1,0) = 2. We apply bit flip mutation to individual (0,1,1,0). What fitness function of mutated individual can be ?**

    a)   1 with 50% probability, 3 with 50% probability

    b)   1 with 90% probability, 3 with 10% probability

    c)   1 with 25% probability, 2 with 50% probability, 3 with 25% probability

Answers

1. c

2. a

Questions

1. In random deviation mutation, we pick random variable with average = 0. Why is it unacceptable to pick random variable with average = 1?

2. Say we are trying to find the maxima of the multivariable function $f(x,y,z)$ with genetic algorithm. Will it be a successful approach to use the shuffle mutation in this case?

Key terms

*   **Random deviation mutation:** Addition of random variable to gene.

*   **Exchange mutation:** Two genes are randomly selected, and their values are exchanged.

*   **Shift mutation:** Shifting random gene left or right.

*   **Bit flip mutation:** Changing the gene bit.

*   **Inversion mutation:** Changing gene subrange order.

*   **Shuffle mutation:** Shuffling gene values in gene subrange.

CHAPTER 6
Effectiveness

In the previous chapter, we studied various methods for constructing GAs. We have seen that different implementations can be used for the same evolutionary action.

Accordingly, there are a vast number of options for constructing a GA. Thus, the following questions arise: How to compare the two architectures of the GA with each other? How do we know that the change we made to the architecture improved its effectiveness in finding a solution? For example, let's take a look at the following *figure 6.1*, where we have two GA architectures:

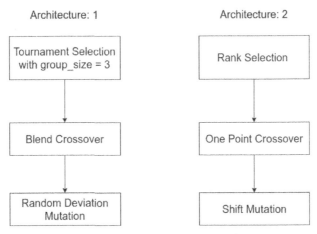

Figure 6.1: *Example of 2 different GA architectures*

In this chapter, we will explore a way to compare the effectiveness of the GA architectures.

Structure

In this chapter, we will cover the following topics:

- Best individual
- Total number of individuals
- Genetic algorithm as random variable
- Monte-Carlo simulation

Objectives

After studying this chapter, you should be able to:

- Understand how to measure the effectiveness of a GA
- Get a clear criteria of GA quality
- Get an intuitive view of the GA as a random variable
- Compare different implementations of GA

6.1 Best individual

So, we formalized the problem, and built the architecture of the GA. What will we consider as the solution to the problem? As a rule, the solution is the individual who has shown the best fitness in the entire history of evolution.

> **NOTE: It is not at all necessary that the best individual will be in the last generation. In evolution, it does not always happen that each subsequent generation is better than the previous one. Therefore, we choose the best from the entire history of evolution.**

Let's study an example of searching for the best individual, and analyzing the population fitness curve's behavior.

Say we want to find the maxima of some complicated function:

$$\sin x \cos x + \left(\frac{|(x+50)(y-10)|}{100}\right)^{0.1}$$

We will keep tracking the best individuals, the average fitness, and the best fitness for each generation `ch6/best_individual.py`.

Define the function we want to study

```python
def func(x, y):
    return sin(x) * cos(x) - pow(abs((x + 50) * (y - 10)) / 10, 0.1)
```

Here we define the individual structure

```python
class Individual:

    def __init__(self, gene_list) -> None:
        self.gene_list = gene_list
        self.fitness = func(self.gene_list[0], self.gene_list[1])

    def __str__(self):
        return f'x: {self.gene_list[0]}, y: {self.gene_list[0]}, fitness: {self.fitness}'
```

Main genetic algorithm operations

```python
def crossover(parent1, parent2):
    child1_genes, child2_genes = crossover_blend(parent1.gene_list, parent2.gene_list, 0.5)
    return Individual(child1_genes), Individual(child2_genes)

def mutate(ind):
    mutated_gene = mutation_random_deviation(ind.gene_list, 0, 1, 0.5)
    return Individual(mutated_gene)

def select(population):
    return selection_tournament(population, group_size = 2)

def create_random():
    return Individual([random.uniform(-100, 100), random.uniform(-100, 100)])
```

GA parameters

```python
POPULATION_SIZE = 10
CROSSOVER_PROBABILITY = .8
MUTATION_PROBABILITY = .1
MAX_GENERATIONS = 25
```

And the main flow of GA

```python
first_population = [create_random() for _ in range(POPULATION_SIZE)]
population = first_population.copy()
```

```
fitness_list = [ind.fitness for ind in population]

fit_avg = [sum(fitness_list) / len(population)]
fit_best = [max(fitness_list)]
fit_best_ever = [max(fitness_list + fit_best)]
best_ind = random.choice(first_population)

generation_number = 0

while generation_number < MAX_GENERATIONS:
    generation_number += 1
    offspring = select(population)
    crossed_offspring = crossover_operation(offspring, crossover,
CROSSOVER_PROBABILITY)
    mutated_offspring = mutation_operation(crossed_offspring, mutate,
MUTATION_PROBABILITY)
    population = mutated_offspring.copy()
    best_ind, fit_avg, fit_best, fit_best_ever = stats(population, best_
ind, fit_avg, fit_best, fit_best_ever)

plot_stats(fit_avg, fit_best, fit_best_ever,
           "Finding maxima of function: \n sin(x) * cos(x) - pow(abs((x
+ 50) * (y - 10)) / 10, 0.1)")
print(f'Best Individual: {best_ind}')
```

Result

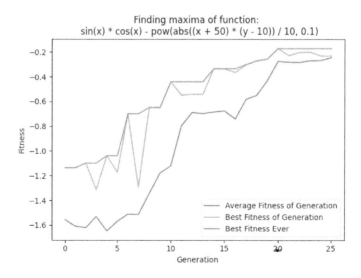

Figure 6.2: Statistics of genetic algorithm action

Our GA finds the following solution, as shown in the preceding *figure 6.2*.

Best Individual: x: -49.57, y: -49.57, fitness: -0.171

Obviously, the metric best fitness ever (that is, best fitness), can be used as a metric of GA effectiveness.

> **NOTE: It is important to note how the curves – the best fitness of the generation and the average fitness of the generation behave. In some generations, these curves can go down, but they go up in the global view. That is why it is essential to take the best individual of the whole history, but not the best of the last generation.**

6.2 Total number of individuals

So, okay, we designed an algorithm that finds an acceptable solution. But at what cost? It should be remembered that GAs are used for problems of a very high dimension, with billions and billions of solutions, and their main feature is speed. If our task is to find the best parameters for the spacecraft hull that satisfies all the constraints and mathematical equations, we can wait a few days and possibly weeks. But if our algorithm every minute solves the airport's routing problems, then we don't have that much time. Of course, computing power grows from year to year, but the tasks are becoming more complicated.

The speed at which the algorithm makes decisions is a critical parameter. In the GA, the most complex operation calculates the fitness function; in turn, the fitness function is calculated once for each individual. Accordingly, the problem of the algorithm's speed can be reduced to the number of individuals required for evolution.

Let's make a few modifications to the example in the previous topic `ch6/number_individuals.py`.

```
class Individual:
    counter = 0

    def __init__(self, gene_list: List[float]) -> None:
        self.gene_list = gene_list
        self.fitness = func(self.gene_list[0], self.gene_list[1])
        self.__class__.counter += 1
```

Result
Total Number of Individuals: 233

NOTE: It is crucial to ensure that the fitness function is calculated only once for each individual. Avoid doing that!

```python
class Individual:

    def fitness(self):

        return sin(self.x) * cos(self.y)
```

This will provoke the fitness function to be recalculated on every call.

6.3 Genetic algorithm as random variable

The GA contains many elements of randomness in its work. It is impossible to tell in advance what decision the GA will come to, in most cases. We can consider the GA as a random variable that returns several values. Please take a look at the following *figure 6.3:*

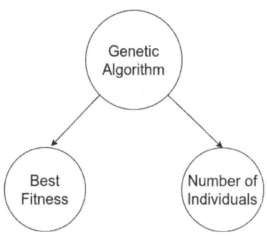

Figure 6.3: *Genetic Algorithm as Random Variable*

The number of individuals is not 100% predictable too. Because GA architecture has parameters like CROSSOVER_PROBABILITY, and MUTATION_PROBABILITY; thus, we don't know in advance how often crossover and mutation occur.

Let's examine the implementation of the GA as a random variable. We will run the GA on the same problem 1000 times, and see the results. We will consider the problem from *Chapter 1: Introduction*, finding the maxima of function sin(x) - |x| / 5 ch6/genetic_algorithm_random_variable.py .

The function we are studying

```python
def func(x):

    return np.sin(x) - .2 * abs(x)
```

Settings of the test

```
random.seed(2)

NUMBER_OF_RUNS = 1000
POPULATION_SIZE = 10
CROSSOVER_PROBABILITY = .8
MUTATION_PROBABILITY = .1
MAX_GENERATIONS = 10
best_fitness_list = []
```

Numerous evaluations of same genetic algorithm

```
best_fitness_list = []

for run in range(NUMBER_OF_RUNS):

    first_population = [create_random() for _ in range(POPULATION_SIZE)]
    best_individual = random.choice(first_population)

    generation_number = 0

    population = first_population.copy()

    while generation_number < MAX_GENERATIONS:
        generation_number += 1
        offspring = select(population)
        crossed_offspring = crossover_operation(offspring, crossover,
CROSSOVER_PROBABILITY)
        mutated_offspring = mutation_operation(crossed_offspring,
mutate, MUTATION_PROBABILITY)
        population = mutated_offspring.copy()

        best_of_generation = max(population, key = lambda ind: ind.
fitness)
        if best_individual.fitness < best_of_generation.fitness:
            best_individual = best_of_generation

    best_fitness_list.append(best_individual.fitness)
    print(f'Best fitness {best_individual.fitness} for {run}')
plt.hist(best_fitness_list, 16, facecolor = 'blue', alpha = 0.5)
plt.show()
```

Result

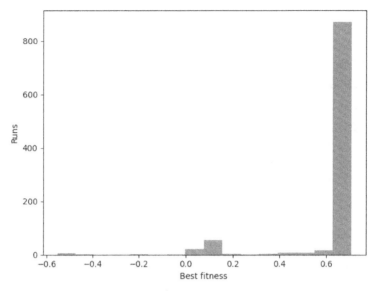

Figure 6.4: Best fitness histogram

As you can see in the preceding *figure 6.4*, in 85% of the cases, the GA finds a solution, the score of which is higher than 0.5. This fact can be a little discouraging, but in more than 10% of cases, the GA finds solutions far from the global maxima.

Let's try to change something in our algorithm, like, increase the number of population, uncomment following line `ch6/genetic_algorithm_random_variable.py`:

```
POPULATION_SIZE = 30
```

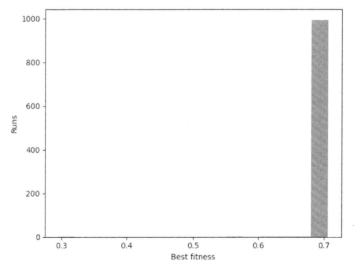

Figure 6.5: Best fitness histogram for GA with population = 30

The preceding *figure 6.5* shows in 99% of the cases, we find the almost best solution. What we did was increase the population size, which means we increased the number of individuals. Accordingly, we slowed down the speed of the algorithm.

Consider how best fitness, and total number of individuals are related. Let's run the same algorithm for different population sizes and analyze dependency on these two parameters ch6/ga_bestfitness_and_numberofindividuals.py:

Settings of GA test

```
POPULATION_SIZE_LIST = range(10, 35, 5)

NUMBER_OF_RUNS = 500

CROSSOVER_PROBABILITY = .8

MUTATION_PROBABILITY = .1

MAX_GENERATIONS = 10
```

GA flow

```
for POPULATION_SIZE in POPULATION_SIZE_LIST:
    best_fitness_list = []
    number_of_individuals = []
    for run in range(NUMBER_OF_RUNS):
        Individual.counter = 0
        first_population = [create_random() for _ in range(POPULATION_
SIZE)]
        best_individual = random.choice(first_population)
        generation_number = 0

        population = first_population.copy()

        while generation_number < MAX_GENERATIONS:
            generation_number += 1
            offspring = select(population)
            crossed_offspring = crossover_operation(offspring,
crossover, CROSSOVER_PROBABILITY)
            mutated_offspring = mutation_operation(crossed_offspring,
mutate, MUTATION_PROBABILITY)
            population = mutated_offspring.copy()

            best_of_generation = max(population, key = lambda ind: ind.
fitness)
            if best_individual.fitness < best_of_generation.fitness:
```

```
                best_individual = best_of_generation

          best_fitness_list.append(best_individual.fitness)
          number_of_individuals.append(Individual.counter)

     plt.scatter(best_fitness_list, number_of_individuals,
               label = f"Distribution for POPULATION SIZE =
{POPULATION_SIZE}")

plt.xlabel('Best Fitness')
plt.ylabel('Number of Individuals')
plt.legend(loc = "upper left")
plt.show()
```

Result

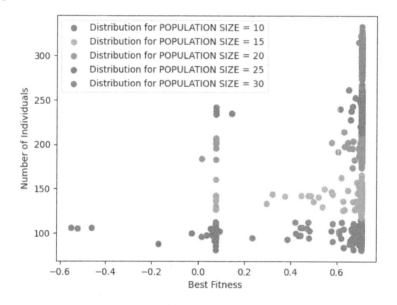

Figure 6.6: Dependency between Number of Individuals and Best Fitness

And we see in the preceding *figure 6.6*, a clear correlation here; the more the number of individuals participate in evolution, the higher the probability that the best fitness parameter will be higher.

GA is a random variable that returns values like – best individual, best fitness, number of individuals. Good GA architecture has the right balance between the high probability of getting acceptable best fitness and a low number of individuals.

6.4 Monte-Carlo simulation

The Monte Carlo method is a method that allows you to obtain the probabilistic characteristics of a random variable through multiple repetitions. In simple words, if we can simulate a random variable's action many times, then with a high degree of confidence, it will be possible to conclude its behavior. In the case of GAs, the following characteristics are significant – average (best fitness), average (number of individuals).

Monte-Carlo simulation applies to multiple repetition tasks when each task can be solved in the foreseeable time. For example, solving routing problems at the airport, optimizing the flight movement of an artificial insect, building an optimal investment portfolio.

Sometimes, GAs are applied to unique problems that are solved just once, and you need to find an acceptable solution only once. Such tasks can be very time-consuming, and it makes no sense for them to answer the questions – How to make the algorithm work effectively? It is important just to find any solution.

The flow of Monte-Carlo simulation can be presented the following way, as shown in *figure 6.7:*

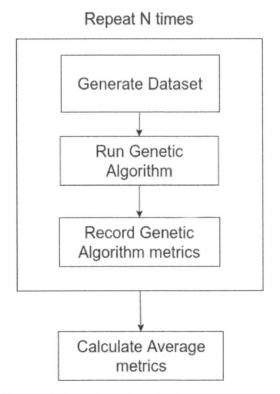

Figure 6.7: *Monte-Carlo Simulation for Genetic Algorithm*

We have an interesting step here called **generate dataset**. That is very important to test the architecture of GA on different datasets, that is, problems, from the same area. If we are testing an implementation of a routing problem solver, we must check it on various route problems. It is possible to test a GA on historical data or to try generating it.

We will use this method in future chapters, and we will see how we can compare different architectures for the same problem.

Conclusion

Although the GA is a random variable, and in most real-life problems, it is impossible to say with 100% accuracy as to which answer will be obtained. We can compute characteristics of the GA efficiency, and compare different implementations with each other.

In the next chapter, we will go through the last aspect of GA architecture – parameter tuning. We already know that GAs have parameters – population size, crossover probability, mutation probability. We will study how they affect the performance of an algorithm.

Points to remember

- Genetic algorithm is a random variable that returns: Best fitness, number of individuals.
- There is a positive correlation between the best fitness and the number of individuals.
- We can compare two different realizations of the GA implementing Monte-Carlo simulation.

Multiple choice questions

1. **In what architecture will the best individual always match the best individual in the last generation?**

    a) Elite selection, fitness driven crossover, fitness driven mutation.

    b) Rank selection, blend crossover, fitness driven mutation.

    c) Just elite selection is enough

2. **We have two different GA architectures, GA1 and GA2, each of them is trying to maximize fitness function. We have three runs of each algorithm with the following results:**

    a) GA1 best fitness : [7, 8, 7]

       b)   GA2 best fitness : [4, 9, 2]

3.   **How can we compare them?**

       a)   GA2 is better because the maxima of GA2 performance is higher than the maxima of GA1 performance

       b)   GA1 is better because the average of GA1 performance is higher than the average of GA2 performance

Answers

1.   a

2.   b

Key terms

- **Best individual:** The solution of the problem obtained by GA.

- **Best fitness:** Measure how well the best individual solves the problem.

- **Number of individuals:** Total number of individuals was generated during evolution.

- **Monte-Carlo simulation:** Probabilistic metric calculation of a GA by multiple simulations.

## CHAPTER 7

Parameter Tuning

The last thing we will learn in designing genetic algorithms before we start solving real problems is studying global algorithm parameters – population size, crossover probability, mutation probability. These parameters govern the dynamics of genetic algorithm flow. We will study each parameter influence, and try to get the intuitive understanding of how each parameter affects the algorithm.

Structure

In this chapter, we will cover the following topics:

- Population size
- Crossover probability
- Mutation probability

Objectives

- Get the intuition about each parameter influence on algorithm flow

7.1 Population size

In previous chapter, we already studied this parameter and concluded that the larger the population size, the higher the probability of finding the best solution. But is it very difficult to maintain a big population. Understanding the effect of population size will help in finding the smallest population size that achieves the best solution.

Each individual can be compared to an explorer who studies the environment in search of the best place – the coordinates of each explorer are determined by his set of genes. Each individual has its own unique set of genes, which means it has its own unique location on the map. The more individuals we have, the higher the probability that someone will find some good place, and spread their location among other individuals, passing its gene set to others; so gradually the entire population will be able to move to the place found by one of the individuals, and continue searching there.

Initially, all individuals are in random places, which from the point of view of fitness functions are of no interest – it's like a desert. One of the individuals finds the river, and the entire population strives for it, but the river also has a lot of different places to stay in terms of suitability, and our population already continues to search in the vicinity of the river. Let's take a look at the following *figure 7.1*:

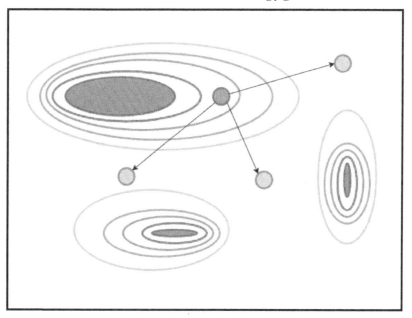

Figure 7.1: One of the individuals notifies other about the place with high fitness value

There is no recipe according to which the optimal population size could be calculated, but it should be understood that the entire population will tend to one point.

Let's look at the heat map of the two variable function *f(x,y)* on the square *[-10, 10]* and try to find its maxima. In this square, we see that there are 2 red zones that are most suitable for the population in terms of the fitness function.

The redder the area, the better the place for the population.

NOTE: We intentionally don't write what this function is. It doesn't matter for us, because the population in search of the best solution does not know anything about the nature and properties of the fitness function, and all that we can do is find out the value of this function at a specific point.

Refer to the following *figure 7.2* for a better understanding:

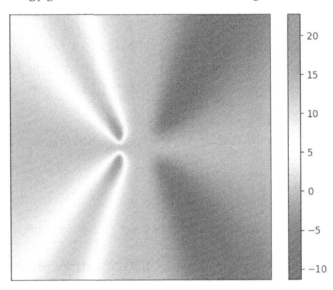

Figure 7.2: Two variable function heat map. Red areas are most appropriate places for the population.

Let's study how population migrates in search of the best place ch7/population_evolution.py.

Import part

```
import random

from typing import List

from numpy import arange

import matplotlib.pyplot as plt

from pylab import meshgrid, cm

from ch7.toolbox import (

    crossover_blend, mutation_random_deviation, constraints, selection_
rank_with_elite,

    crossover_operation,

    mutation_operation,

)
```

Definition of 2-D function surface

```
def func(x, y):
    return - 10 * pow(x * y, 2) * x / (3 * pow(x * x * x / 4 + 1, 2) +
pow(y, 4) + 1)
```

Structure of individual

```
class Individual:

    def __init__(self, gene_list: List[float]) -> None:
        self.gene_list = [constraints(g) for g in gene_list]
        self.fitness = func(self.gene_list[0], self.gene_list[1])

    def __str__(self):
        return f'x: {self.gene_list[0]}, y: {self.gene_list[0]}, fitness:
{self.fitness}'
```

Basic GA operations

```
def crossover(parent1, parent2):
    child1_genes, child2_genes = crossover_blend(parent1.gene_list,
parent2.gene_list, 0.5)
    return Individual(child1_genes), Individual(child2_genes)

def mutate(ind):
    mutated_gene = mutation_random_deviation(ind.gene_list, 0, 1, 0.5)
    return Individual(mutated_gene)

def select(population):
    return selection_rank_with_elite(population, elite_size = 2)

def create_random():
    return Individual([round(random.uniform(-10, 10), 2), round(random.
uniform(-10, 10), 2)])
```

Parameter set

```
POPULATION_SIZE_LIST = [6, 10, 20, 50]

CROSSOVER_PROBABILITY = .8

MUTATION_PROBABILITY = .2

MAX_GENERATIONS = 10
```

Main GA flow

```
for POPULATION_SIZE in POPULATION_SIZE_LIST:
    first_population = [create_random() for _ in range(POPULATION_SIZE)]
    best_ind = random.choice(first_population)
    generation_number = 0

    population = first_population.copy()

    while generation_number < MAX_GENERATIONS:

        generation_number += 1

        offspring = select(population)
        crossed_offspring = crossover_operation(offspring, crossover,
CROSSOVER_PROBABILITY)
        mutated_offspring = mutation_operation(crossed_offspring,
mutate, MUTATION_PROBABILITY)
        population = mutated_offspring.copy()

        best_of_generation = max(population, key = lambda ind: ind.
fitness)
        if best_ind.fitness < best_of_generation.fitness:
            best_ind = best_of_generation

        im = plt.imshow(Z, cmap = cm.bwr, extent = [-10, 10, -10, 10])
        plt.colorbar(im)
        plt.xticks([])
        plt.yticks([])
        plt.title(f"Population size: {POPULATION_SIZE}, Generation:
{generation_number} \n"
                  f"Best Individual: {round(best_ind.fitness), 2}")
        plt.scatter([ind.gene_list[0] for ind in population], [ind.gene_
list[1] for ind in population], color = 'black')
        plt.show()

    print(f'Best Individual : {best_ind} for population size:
{POPULATION_SIZE}')
```

Let's study the migration of the population with size 6, as shown in the following *figure 7.3*:

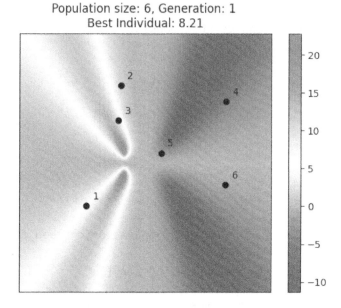

Figure 7.3: *Generation 1 of Population size 6*

Here we see 2 individuals -- #1 and #3 that are in the red zone. Look what happens in the next generation (refer to the following *figure 7.4*):

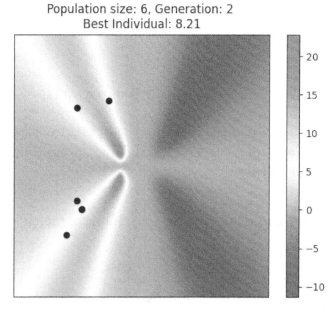

Figure 7.4: *Generation 2 of Population size 6*

We see that the left bottom individual passed the positive information to other individuals, and now there are three individuals near the bottom red zone. Take a look at the following *figure 7.5:*

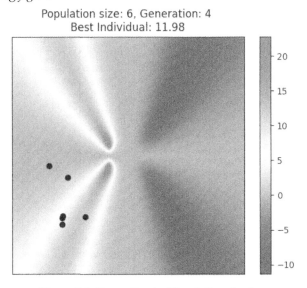

Figure 7.5: *Generation 4 of Population size 6*

In the fourth generation, we see the entire population begins to concentrate near the lower red zone.

Now let's take a look at the following *figure 7.6* to see what happens in the fifth generation:

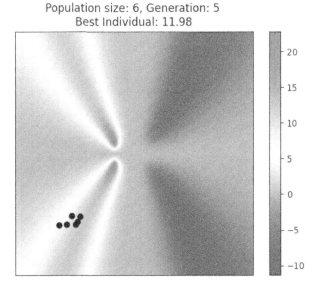

Figure 7.6: *Generation 5 of Population size 6*

And here in the fifth-generation, the whole population is concentrated in one area. This area is good, but far from the best.

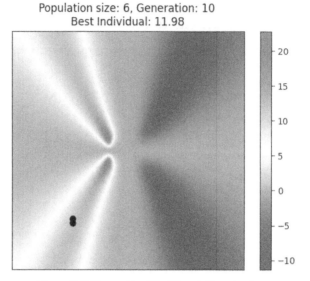

Figure 7.7: Generation 10 of Population size 6

In the last generation as shown in the preceding *figure 7.7*, the entire population took on a uniform appearance at almost one point, and it is unlikely that it will move anywhere from there.

Now, let's study the evolution path of population size 10. Take a look at the following *figure 7.8:*

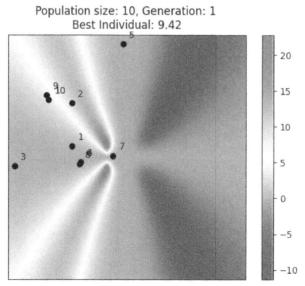

Figure 7.8: Generation 1 of Population size 1

Pay attention that there is one individual #2 in the top red zone and two individuals, #9 and #10 at the border of the red zone.

Let's look at the following *figure 7.9*:

Population size: 10, Generation: 2
Best Individual: 12.33

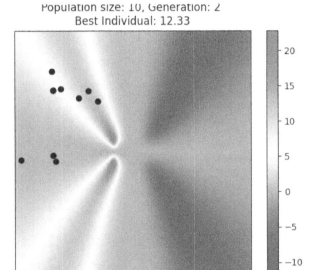

Figure 7.9: Generation 2 of Population size 10

Individuals #2, #9, and #10 have passed positive information to another part of the population, and in the second generation, the largest part of the population is being concentrated at the red area.

Look at the following *figure 7.10* to know what happens in the last generation:

Population size: 10, Generation: 10
Best Individual: 12.54

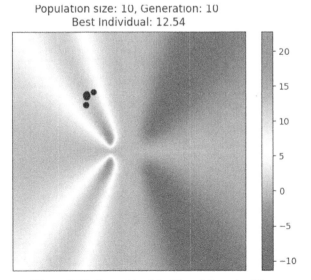

Figure 7.10: Generation 10 of Population size 10

Evolution finishes in a similar manner like the evolution for 6 individuals in the population, but evolution with 10 individuals has found a slightly better solution than the previous one.

Looking at the evolution path of the population with size 20 (following *figure 7.11*), we can see that this population achieves the *"top of the hill"*, and almost the whole population located near the top.

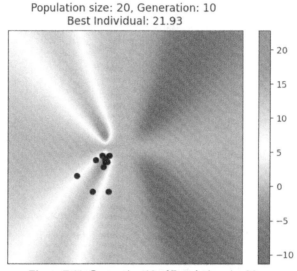

Figure 7.11: Generation 10 of Population size 20

Ok, the population size = 20 seems a rather good option, but let's see what happens if the number of individuals is equal to 50. Refer to the following *figure 7.12:*

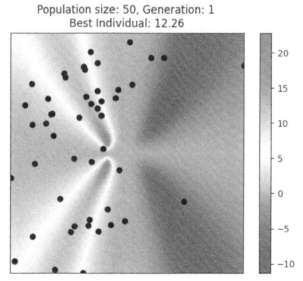

Figure 7.12: Generation 1 of Population size 50

Ok, in the next-generation, we do expect some positive genetic moves (following *figure 7.13*):

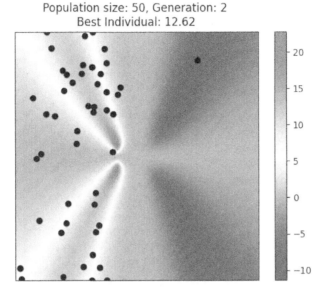

Figure 7.13: *Generation 2 of Population size 50*

Maybe it is not easy to notice, but there is some positive genetic move, a lot of individuals have left the blue zone, and everything is fine so far; let's see what is happening next (following *figure 7.14*):

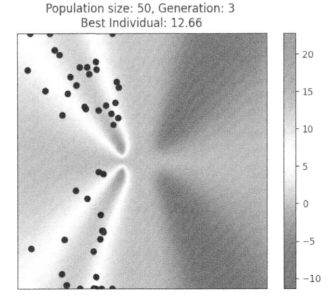

Figure 7.14: *Generation 3 of Population size 50*

Yes, there is some positive movement, but we expected maybe a more drastic change; let's skip some iterations, and see what happens in the sixth generation (following *figure 7.15*):

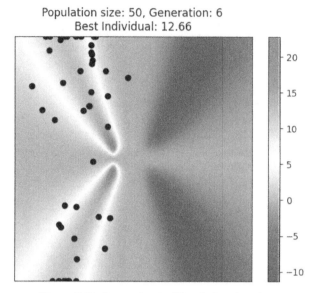

Figure 7.15: *Generation 6 of Population size 50*

Still no global progress! The situation becomes even worse if we notice that the best individual for the 6th generation of population sized 50 is just the same as the best individual for 2nd generation of population sized 20. This may seem like a very strange result. Let's examine the last generation (following *figure 7.16*):

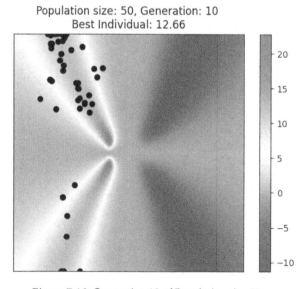

Figure 7.16: *Generation 10 of Population size 50*

This is a totally unacceptable solution for such a large amount of calculation. Evolution with 6 and 10 individuals has shown almost the same best fitness result.

Let's get an intuitive understanding of this paradox. Small populations are more easily influenced by one or more leaders. It is enough for one or several individuals to find an acceptable place, which then makes it is easier for them to call the entire population. In case of a large population, there is a lot of noise. Different individuals call others to completely different places, and most call on, not to move anywhere at all. Large populations have very high inertia and take much longer to organize themselves. Take a look at the following *figure 7.17*:

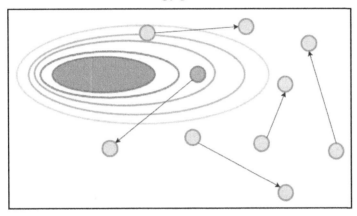

Figure 7.17: *Genetic communication noise*

Now you may think that large populations are not suitable for organized search at all. But we have another paradox here. Look at the last generation of population sized 50. It seems that this population has no change to *"climb on the top of the hill"*, but let's look at what will happen after 200 generations (following *figure 7.18*):

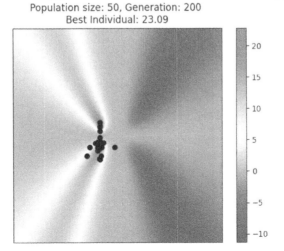

Figure 7.18: *Generation 200 of Population size 50*

This population has found both absolutely best solutions! It seemed that there was no chance for this to happen, but it happens. Larger populations take much longer to organize themselves, but are able to construct much more complex solutions.

Smaller population moves faster, but gets stuck earlier.

Larger population moves slower, but keeps moving farther than the smaller ones and constructs more complicated solutions.

7.2 Crossover probability

Crossover is a mechanism for the exchange of information between two individuals. In the architecture of the GA, individuals make a crossover with a certain probability. Let's study what the crossover probability is, and how it affects the evolution of the population.

Let's say we have two individuals that have passed the selection, which means it is highly possible that those two individuals already have something valuable in their genes. And in the next step, the following can happen:

- Either with probability p, they can make a crossover, thereby making an attempt to generate a new solution, perhaps a fundamentally new solution that will greatly help the population in the process of evolution.
- Or with probability 1-p they can do self-cloning to allow good individuals to develop further without any crossover.

This probability p is called crossover probability. Take a look at the following *figure 7.19:*

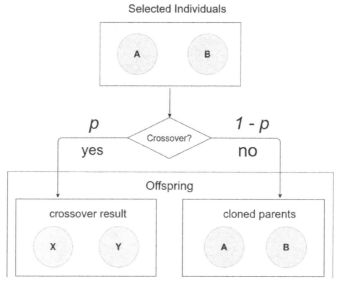

Figure 7.19: Crossover Probability

There is always a risk that the crossover will be unsuccessful and the offspring will not only not give anything useful for the rest of the population, but will also lose what the parents had; therefore, crossover itself can both increase the average fitness function of the population and lower it.

Let's study the variations of the evolution to find the maxima of some function f(x,y) for different values of crossover probability. Refer to the following *figure 7.20:*

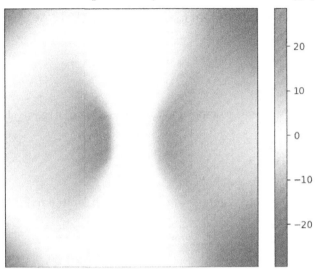

Figure 7.20: *Two variable function heat map. Red areas are the most appropriate places for the population.*

Our function f(x,y) has only one peak, and thus it is rather easy to find its maxima; let's take a look ch7/crossover_evolution.py:

Import part

```
import random
from typing import List
from numpy import arange
import matplotlib.pyplot as plt
from pylab import meshgrid, cm
from ch7.toolbox import (
    crossover_blend, mutation_random_deviation, constraints, selection_
rank_with_elite, crossover_operation, mutation_operation)
```

Definition of 2-D function surface

```
def func(x, y):
    return - 10 * (pow(x, 5) / (3 * pow(x * x * x / 4 + 1, 2) + pow(y,
4) + 10) + pow(x * y / 2, 2) / 1000)
```

Structure of individual

```python
class Individual:
    counter = 0

    def __init__(self, gene_list: List[float]) -> None:
        self.gene_list = [constraints(g) for g in gene_list]
        self.fitness = round(func(self.gene_list[0], self.gene_list[1]), 2)
        self.__class__.counter += 1
        self.id = self.__class__.counter

    def __str__(self):
        return f'x: {self.gene_list[0]}, y: {self.gene_list[0]}, fitness: {self.fitness}'
```

Basic GA operations

```python
def crossover(parent1, parent2):
    child1_genes, child2_genes = crossover_blend(parent1.gene_list, parent2.gene_list, 0.8)
    return Individual(child1_genes), Individual(child2_genes)


def mutate(ind):
    mutated_gene = mutation_random_deviation(ind.gene_list, 0, 1, 0.5)
    return Individual(mutated_gene)


def select(population):
    return selection_rank_with_elite(population, elite_size = 2)


def create_random():
    return Individual([round(random.uniform(-10, 10), 2), round(random.uniform(-10, 10), 2)])
```

Parameter set

```python
POPULATION_SIZE = 16
CROSSOVER_PROBABILITIES = [.0, .4, .7]
MUTATION_PROBABILITY = .2
MAX_GENERATIONS = 10
```

The main GA flow

```python
for CROSSOVER_PROBABILITY in CROSSOVER_PROBABILITIES:
    first_population = [create_random() for _ in range(POPULATION_SIZE)]
```

```python
    best_individual = random.choice(first_population)
    generation_number = 0

    population = first_population.copy()

    while generation_number < MAX_GENERATIONS:
        generation_number += 1
        offspring = select(population)
        crossed_offspring = crossover_operation(offspring, crossover,
CROSSOVER_PROBABILITY)
        mutated_offspring = mutation_operation(crossed_offspring,
mutate, MUTATION_PROBABILITY)
        population = mutated_offspring.copy()

        best_of_generation = max(population, key = lambda ind: ind.
fitness)
        if best_individual.fitness < best_of_generation.fitness:
            best_individual = best_of_generation

        im = plt.imshow(Z, cmap = cm.bwr, extent = [-10, 10, -10, 10])
        plt.colorbar(im)
        plt.xticks([])
        plt.yticks([])
        plt.title(f"Crossover Probability: {CROSSOVER_PROBABILITY},
Generation: {generation_number} \n"
                    f"Best Individual: {best_individual.fitness}")
        plt.scatter([ind.gene_list[0] for ind in population],
                    [ind.gene_list[1] for ind in population],
                    color = 'black')
        plt.show()

    print(f'Best Individual : {best_individual} for crossover
probability: {CROSSOVER_PROBABILITY}')
```

Let's look at the evolution of population with crossover probability equal to 0 (no crossover); refer to the following *figure 7.21:*

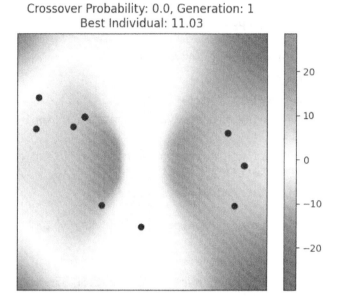

Figure 7.21: Generation 1 with Crossover Probability 0

In the first generation after first selection, there are a lot of individuals in red area, further evolution seems to be promising (following *figure 7.22):*

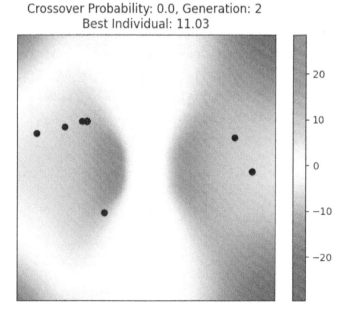

Figure 7.22: Generation 2 with Crossover Probability 0

After second generation, more individuals are in the red zone, but they are located in one small area.

> **NOTE: You may think that** *figure 7.22* **has fewer individuals than what** *figure 7.21* **has. That happens because in our GA architecture, there are a lot of duplicates, that is, there are several individuals at one point.**

Now, let's take a look at the following *figure 7.23*:

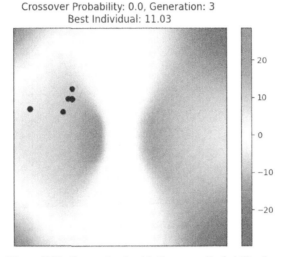

Figure 7.23: *Generation 3 with Crossover Probability 0*

In the third generation, the entire population begins to concentrate in some area, but this area is far from the peak that we would like to find. Take a look at the following *figure 7.24:*

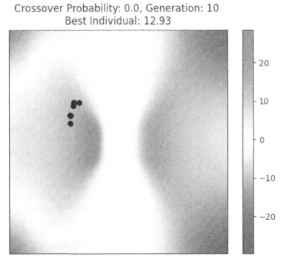

Figure 7.24: *Generation 10 with Crossover Probability 0*

In the last generation, practically there is no improvement over the 3rd generation. Why does this happen? The entire population rushed to individuals that were the best in the very first generation. The solution randomly found at the very beginning practically did not change. This was all because of the lack of crossover. The population did not have the opportunity to diversify its genes at the expense of others, possibly even bad, individuals. An architecture without crossover is highly likely to quickly get the population stuck in one area, possibly very far from optimal.

Let's look at the evolution with probability equal to 0.4 (following *figure 7.25*):

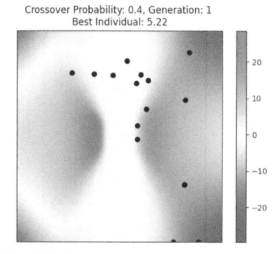

Figure 7.25: *Generation 1 with Crossover Probability 0.4*

After first generation, we have very unfortunate initial position of individuals. Only one individual is in the red zone. Now, let's take a look at the following *figure 7.26:*

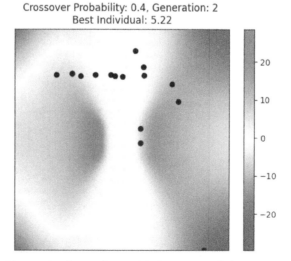

Figure 7.26: *Generation 2 with Crossover Probability 0.4*

In the second generation, individuals make the positive movement, but the best individual still shows no improvement.

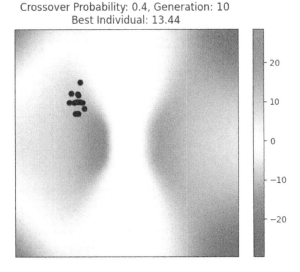

Figure 7.27: Generation 10 with Crossover Probability 0.4

In the last generation as shown in the preceding *figure 7.27*, the individuals we see that again populate is located near the best solution of first generation. There is no significant improvement over the non-crossover architecture.

Architecture with crossover probability equal to 0.7 has more interesting evolution. Take a look at the following *figure 7.28*:

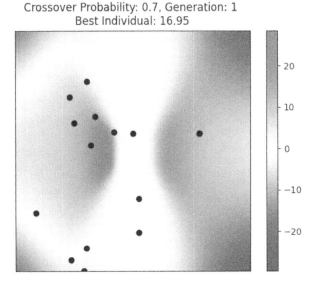

Figure 7.28: Generation 1 with Crossover Probability 0.7

After the first generation, there are a lot of individuals in the red area, but the evolution process due to the high probability of crossover keeps searching for new solutions (as shown in the following *figure 7.29*):

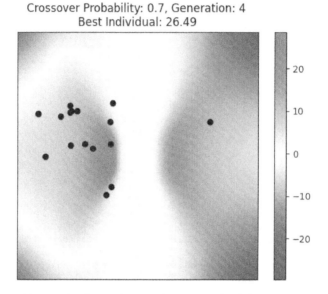

Figure 7.29: Generation 4 with Crossover Probability 0.7

After the seventh generation, the whole population is distributed in the red zone. It increases the probability of finding best solution drastically.

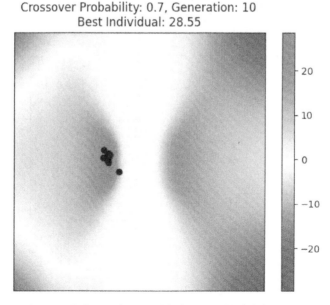

Figure 7.30: Generation 10 with Crossover Probability 0.7

Finally, as shown in the preceding *figure 7.30,* the whole population has covered the top of the hill.

Crossover probability defines the degree of population variability. The higher the crossover probability, the stronger the population's craving for new solutions. The danger of a higher number of crosses is the loss of useful accumulated hereditary factors.

7.3 Mutation probability

If the crossover is an attempt to create a new solution based on two existing solutions, then mutation is a completely random deviation that does not necessarily add something useful to the individual but is necessary for the constant search for the best solutions.

The mutation probability is the probability with which an individual in a new population will be mutated. Refer to the following *figure 7.31:*

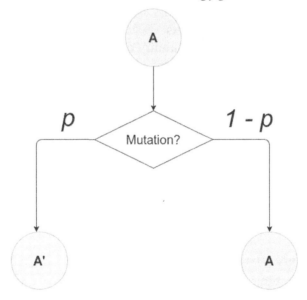

Figure 7.31: *Mutation Probability*

Let's study the variations of the evolution to find the maxima of some function f(x,y) for different values of mutation probability.

Take a look at the following *figure 7.32:*

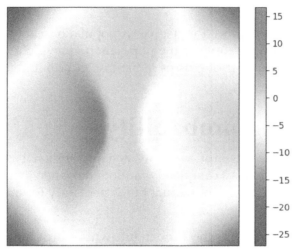

Figure 7.32: Two variable function heat map. Red areas are the most appropriate places for the population.

We will evaluate three types of GAs -- without mutation, with 0.3 mutation probability, and with 1 mutation probability `ch7/mutation_evolution.py`.

Import part

```
import random
from typing import List
from numpy import arange
import matplotlib.pyplot as plt
from pylab import meshgrid, cm
from ch7.toolbox import (
    crossover_blend, mutation_random_deviation, constraints, selection_rank_with_elite,
    crossover_operation,
    mutation_operation,
)
```

Definition of 2-D function surface

```
def func(x, y):
    return - 10 * (pow(x, 5) / (3 * pow(x * x * x / 3 + 1, 2) + pow(y, 4) + 10) + pow(x * y / 2, 2) / 1000) + x / 2
```

Structure of individual

```
class Individual:
    counter = 0
```

```
    def __init__(self, gene_list: List[float]) -> None:
        self.gene_list = [constraints(g) for g in gene_list]
        self.fitness = round(func(self.gene_list[0], self.gene_list[1]),
2)

        self.__class__.counter += 1
        self.id = self.__class__.counter

    def __str__(self):
        return f'x: {self.gene_list[0]}, y: {self.gene_list[0]}, fitness:
{self.fitness}'
```

Basic GA operations

```
def crossover(parent1, parent2):
    child1_genes, child2_genes = crossover_blend(parent1.gene_list,
parent2.gene_list, 0.8)
    return Individual(child1_genes), Individual(child2_genes)

def mutate(ind):
    mutated_gene = mutation_random_deviation(ind.gene_list, 0, 1, 0.8)
    return Individual(mutated_gene)

def select(population):
    return selection_rank_with_elite(population, elite_size = 2)

def create_random():
    return Individual([round(random.uniform(-10, 10), 2), round(random.
uniform(-10, 10), 2)])
```

Parameter set

```
POPULATION_SIZE = 8
CROSSOVER_PROBABILITY = .8
MUTATION_PROBABILITIES = [0, .3, 1]
MAX_GENERATIONS = 10
```

Main GA flow

```
for MUTATION_PROBABILITY in MUTATION_PROBABILITIES:
    first_population = [create_random() for _ in range(POPULATION_SIZE)]
    best_individual = random.choice(first_population)
    generation_number = 0
```

```
    population = first_population.copy()

    while generation_number < MAX_GENERATIONS:

        generation_number += 1

        offspring = select(population)
        crossed_offspring = crossover_operation(offspring, crossover,
CROSSOVER_PROBABILITY)
        mutated_offspring = mutation_operation(crossed_offspring,
mutate, MUTATION_PROBABILITY)
        population = mutated_offspring.copy()

        best_of_generation = max(population, key = lambda ind: ind.
fitness)
        if best_individual.fitness < best_of_generation.fitness:
            best_individual = best_of_generation

        im = plt.imshow(Z, cmap = cm.bwr, extent = [-10, 10, -10, 10])
        plt.colorbar(im)
        plt.xticks([])
        plt.yticks([])
        plt.title(f"Mutation Probability: {MUTATION_PROBABILITY},
Generation: {generation_number} \n"
                  f"Best Individual: {best_individual.fitness}")
        plt.scatter([ind.gene_list[0] for ind in population],
                    [ind.gene_list[1] for ind in population],
                    color = 'black')
        plt.show()

    print(f'Best Individual : {best_individual} for mutation
probability: {MUTATION_PROBABILITY}')
```

For the first generation we have the following (refer to *figure 7.33*):

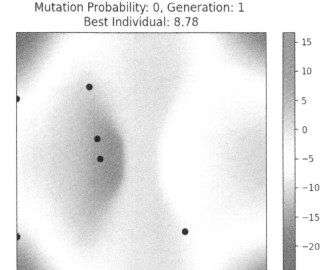

Figure 7.33: *Generation 1 with Mutation Probability 0*

After first generation, two individuals are very close to the top of the hill.

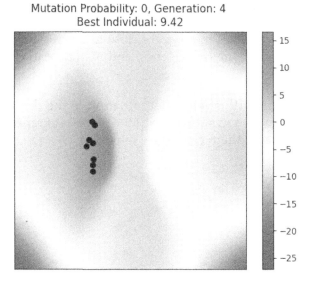

Figure 7.34: *Generation 4 with Mutation Probability 0*

After four generations (as shown in the preceding *figure 7.34*), almost all individuals are on the same line; we need just one to slightly move right. But what will cause at least one individual to move to the right? All individuals have practically the same x-coordinate gene value. After crossover, x-coordinate will practically not change. But we have no mutations! There is no way for any individual to move to the right occasionally, to get useful information, and pass it to other individuals. And after 10 generations, we get a predictable situation, as shown in the following *figure 7.35:*

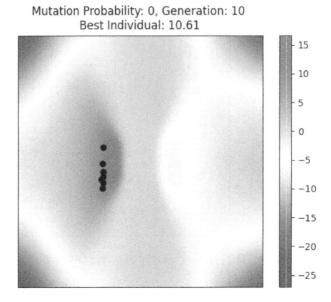

Figure 7.35: Generation 10 with Mutation Probability 0

As we assumed, a population that is very close to the best solution, cannot find it. The population has fixed one of its genes, and is unable to change it without the mutation.

> NOTE: This example illustrates that mutation is the driving force behind evolution. Some species in nature have mechanisms of reproduction without crossover, but none of them can refuse mutation.

Let's go next to a population with positive mutation probability equal to 0.3. Take a look at the following *figure 7.36:*

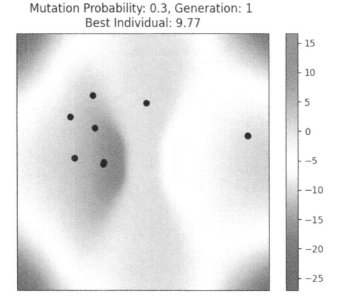

Figure 7.36: *Generation 1 with Mutation Probability 0.3*

Initial distribution of individuals is close to the distribution we had for previous evolution without mutation.

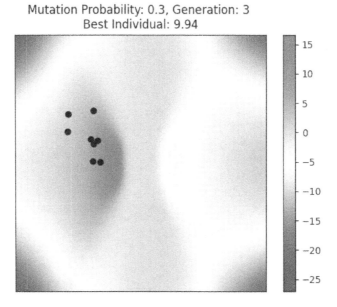

Figure 7.37: *Generation 3 with Mutation Probability 0.3*

As shown in the preceding *figure 7.37*, after the third generation, we have a very similar situation; the population needs to make any movement to the right, and due to mutation, it makes this move. Take a look at the following *figure 7.38* for the final generation:

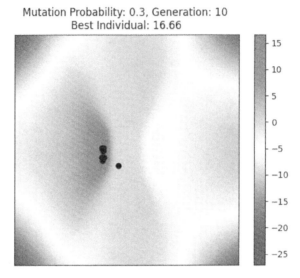

Figure 7.38: Generation 10 with Mutation Probability 0.3

Finally, we see that population with positive mutation probability has found the best solution to the problem.

But is a large number of mutations always a good thing? Let's take a look at the following *figure 7.39*:

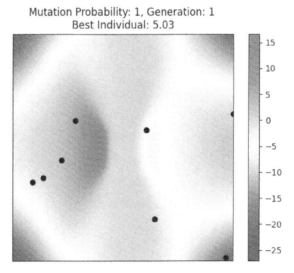

Figure 7.39: Generation 1 with Mutation Probability 1

Well, here after the first-generation, the population is distributed rather successfully, and it seems that it should adapt to the fitness function the best way, but:

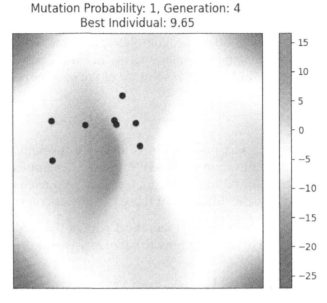

Figure 7.40: *Generation 4 with Mutation Probability 1*

As shown in the preceding *figure 7.40*, mutation on each individual gives too much randomness, as a result of which, the population can't fix any positive pattern.

Now, let's take a look at the following *figure 7.41*:

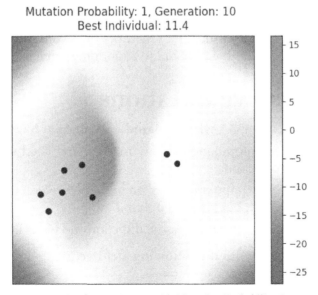

Figure 7.41: *Generation 10 with Mutation Probability 1*

The evolution with very high mutation probability looks like a random search . Every individual which has any positive information can be mutated afterward, losing the genetic data it had obtained.

Mutation probability defines the degree of population deviations. It is almost impossible to find any solution to complex problems without the mutation mechanism. On the other hand, too many frequent mutations disrupt the forward evolutionary movement, and leads the solution of the problem to a random search.

Conclusion

The right combination of GA parameters is just as important as the selection of breeding, crossing, and mutation methods. Initially, it is impossible to say which parameters will be best suited for a specific task, but in this chapter, we presented mechanisms for studying the influence of these parameters on evolutionary search.

We have completed the study of the theoretical part of the GA design. In the next section, we will move on to learning how to solve real-world problems.

Points to remember

- Smaller population moves faster, but gets stuck earlier.
- Larger population moves slower, but can obtain more complicated solutions.
- The higher the crossover probability, the stronger the population's craving for new solutions. The danger of a large number of crosses is the loss of useful accumulated hereditary factors.
- GA should have positive mutation probability.
- Too high a mutation probability disrupts the evolutionary movement, and leads the solution of the problem to a random search.

Multiple choice questions

1. **What troubles can GA with too large a population have?**

   a) Too large a population is very inertial, and need more time to obtain correct direction.

   b) Too large a population has premature convergence, that is, it finds solution fast, but far from optimal.

   c) Too large a population has no direction and looks like a random search.

2. **Say we have GA with the following architecture:**

   population size = 2

   crossover probability = 0

mutation probability = 1

Elite selection

Fitness driven random deviation mutation with average = 0 and sigma = 0.01

Initial generation looks like the following *figure 7.42:*

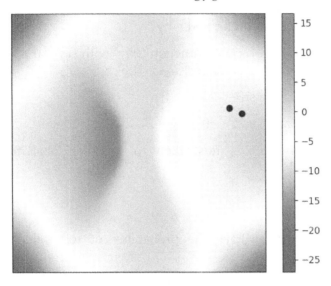

Figure 7.42: *Initial generation*

Is it possible that this GA will find global maxima after 1 million generations?

a) Yes, it is surely possible, because mutation probability = 1 will produce random walk, and it is highly likely that one of these individuals will find the global maxima.

b) No, it is impossible because fitness driven mutation has a condition not to produce mutations that are worse than the current individual. But in the first generation, two individuals are located on the red island, and due to low sigma = 0.01 in random deviation mutation, they cannot jump over the white line to the other red island.

Answers

1. a
2. b

Questions

1. If you had a choice in GA design:

    - to set crossover probability = 0 (i.e. exclude crossover)

    - to set mutation probability = 0 (i.e. exclude mutation)

    Which would you prefer and why?

2. Say we have two variable function f(x,y) with several maximum, and there are two identical GA architectures:

    - with population size = 20

    - with population size = 50

    Which architecture is most likely to find the global maximum after 500 generations?

Key terms

-   **Crossover probability:** The probability of two selected individuals to generate new offspring.

-   **Mutation probability:** The probability of individual mutation in new generation.

CHAPTER 8
Black-Box Function

The most common task is to find the parameters at which a particular function reaches its maxima values. Often these functions have a very complex analytical form, and sometimes nothing is known at all about the function itself, and it is represented as a black-box. In this chapter, we will study the methods that help in finding values at which a certain function takes its maxima value.

Structure

In this chapter, we will cover the following topics:

- What is black-box function
- Gene encodings
- Genetic algorithm architecture

Objectives

After studying this chapter, you should be able to:

- Get the understanding about what the black-box function is
- Explore ways to create individuals for various optimizable functions
- Examine the most suitable genetic algorithm architectures for searching maxima of a black-box function

8.1 What is Black-box function?

In all aspects of life, we are facing various functions. Sometimes the nature of these functions is very clear, and can be expressed as an explicit mathematical formula; this formula can be rather simple. For example, *5–x2*, or the rather complicated:

$$2 \cos \frac{1}{x} \left(e\sqrt{x} + x \right) \cos \frac{1}{2} \left(2 - \int_0^x \lim_{n \to \infty} \left(1 + \frac{1}{ne^x} \right)^x \right)$$

In some cases, functions are expressed using the following programming code:

```python
import math
```

```python
def dummy_function(x):
    even_sum = 0
    even_count = 0
    prod = 1
    for d in str(x):
        digit = int(d)
        prod *= digit
        if digit % 2 == 0:
            even_sum += digit
            even_count += 1
    return math.factorial(even_sum) * x / prod**even_count
```

But there are also cases when we generally have a poor idea of the function's nature, and how it is calculated. For example, we have a very complex device and four inputs for supplying voltage, and at the output, we receive a certain amount of heat. We have no idea about how this device works inside, but we need to achieve such voltage parameters at which the temperature released will be maximum.

We often do not need to spend time on the long-term analytical, and mathematical study of a function. This study can take weeks, months, or even years. We just need to find the parameters at which the value of the function is maxima. In this case, we can consider the function as some kind of black box that has some input parameters, and one output value. We will call any function of several variables $f(x1, x2, \ldots, xn)$ of unknown nature as a black-box function.

> **NOTE: As we mentioned earlier, there is a rich mathematical toolset for finding the maxima for classical differentiable functions. It can be much more efficient than the use of genetic algorithms. There are some exceptions for complicated functions with boundary conditions in the form of differential equations; for finding the extrema of these functions, the use of genetic algorithms is reasonable.**

Before finding the maxima of a function, it is sometimes necessary to make certain transformations.

We always mention the search of the maxima of function f, but what if we need to find the minima of a function f? In this case, we are simply looking for the maxima of the function -f. Hereinafter, we will consider only the search for the maxima.

Another detail worth mentioning is that you should always limit the range of values of an individual's genes in advance. There should not be a situation where an individual's gene can take values in a range: (-∞, +∞), (-∞, a] or [a, +∞). This is done in order to limit the search range initially, and not allow the population to go beyond certain limits that do not need to be investigated a priori.

In order to not inject these restrictions on the operations of crossover and mutation, you can add range restrictions when initializing an individual:

```python
def range_limit(g, min_v, max_v):
    return max(min(g, max_v), min_v)


class Individual:

    def __init__(self, gene_list) -> None:
        self.gene_list = [
            range_limit(gene_list[0], 0, 10),
            range_limit(gene_list[1], 10, 10),
            range_limit(gene_list[2], 0, 100),
        ]
```

8.2 Gene encodings

Here we look at the most common function parameters, and how they are encoded in an individual's genes.

Real encoding

The simplest and most convenient way is when a gene is a real-valued limited value. These genes are convenient in that we can apply convenient methods of crossover, and mutation without modification. These genes are the parameters for solving the problem, represented by the float type. Until now, in all the examples above, we have considered only such genes.

For example, individuals in a population searching for the maxima of the function cos(x)sin(y) will use real encoded genes.

Discrete encoding

Discrete encoding is used to represent finite linearly ordered sets. For example:

[-10, -9, -8, ..., 10] or [0, 2, 4, ..., 100].

This type of set is used in many functions. For example, if we consider a function f(age, word_count) that returns the number of likes on Facebook made by the user aged "age", and word_count is the number of words in a post that received a like. For discrete encoded genes, we can use standard crossover and mutation operations with the selection of the most appropriate element in the set.

Let's study the discrete encoding implementation ch8/discrete_genes.py.

This method will be responsible for the selection of an appropriate allowed set element:

```
def closest(value, value_list):
    return min(value_list, key = lambda x: abs(x - value))
```

Next, we define the individual itself with an allowed set of values for each gene:

```
class Individual:
    x_set = range(-10, 11)
    y_set = range(0, 1000, 2)

    def __init__(self, gene_list):
        self.gene_list = [closest(gene_list[0], self.x_set),
closest(gene_list[1], self.y_set)]

    def __str__(self):
        return str(self.gene_list)
```

And here we have the classical operations flow:

```
if __name__ == '__main__':

    random.seed(3)

    ind1 = create_random()
    ind2 = create_random()
    print(f'Individual 1: {ind1}')
    print(f'Individual 2: {ind2}')

    c1_genes, c2_genes = crossover_blend(ind1.gene_list, ind2.gene_list,
0.2)
    child1, child2 = Individual(c1_genes), Individual(c2_genes)
```

```
print(f'Child 1: {child1}')
print(f'Child 1: {child2}')

mut1 = Individual(mutation_random_deviation(child1.gene_list, 0, 2, .5))
mut2 = Individual(mutation_random_deviation(child2.gene_list, 0, 2, .5))
print(f'Mutant 1: {mut1}')
print(f'Mutant 2: {mut2}')
```

Result

Individual 1	-3	606
Individual 2	7	132
Child 1	0	452
Child 2	3	80
Mutant 1	1	450
Mutant 2	3	82

It should be understood that with discrete gene encoding, the mutation mechanism works in gaps, and not smoothly, as in the case of real-gene encoding. This feature can eliminate the mutation at all . This is rather a common mistake in GA design. Let's show an example ch8/impossible_mutation.py.

Say we have a random deviation mutation with uniform random variable on range *(-1, 1)*:

```
def mutation_random_uniform_deviation(ind):
    mut = copy.deepcopy(ind)
    for i in range(len(mut)):
        mut[i] = mut[i] + random.uniform(-1, 1)
    return mut
```

Discrete encoded individual:

```
class DiscreteIndividual:
    x_set = range(-1000, 1001, 2)

    def __init__(self, gene_list):
        self.gene_list = [closest(gene_list[0], self.x_set)]
```

Real encoded individual:

```
class RealIndividual:
    def __init__(self, gene_list):
        self.gene_list = gene_list
```

And let's make one thousand mutation iterations:

```
if __name__ == '__main__':

    random.seed(5)

    disc_ind = DiscreteIndividual([0])
    real_ind = RealIndividual([0])

    for _ in range(0, 1000):
        real_ind = RealIndividual(mutation_random_uniform_
deviation(real_ind.gene_list))
        disc_ind = DiscreteIndividual(mutation_random_uniform_
deviation(disc_ind.gene_list))

    print(f'Discrete Individual: {disc_ind.gene_list}')
    print(f'Real Individual: {real_ind.gene_list}')
```

Result

Discrete Individual	0
Real Individual	-10.597549227297753

As we see, discrete individual is not mutated, because any random deviation cannot make any discrete shift of gene. Refer to the following *figure 8.1:*

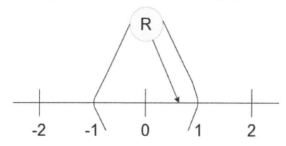

Figure 8.1: *Uniform Random Deviation for Discrete Gene Encoding*

The random deviation can produce any value lower than 1, but for shifting from 0 to 2, we need deviation greater or equal than 1.

Enumeration encoding

In some cases, a function can take input parameters that can be considered as enumeration. Let's study the following function:

```
def enum_function(fun_name, x, n):
```

```
if fun_name == 'cos':
    return math.cos(x)**n
elif fun_name == 'sin':
    return math.sin(x)**n
elif fun_name == 'log':
    return math.log(x, 2)**n
elif fun_name == 'exp':
    return math.exp(x)**n
else:
    raise Exception(f'Unknown Function: {fun_name}')
```

This function takes the parameter fun_name, which defines the function to be represented in the formula. This parameter can take values – cos, sin, log, exp.

For enumerated genes encoding we can use only uniform crossover, which changes values in parent genes.

As a mutation, the function of a random choice of the value in the enumeration set can be used. Let's take a look at the following *figure 8.2:*

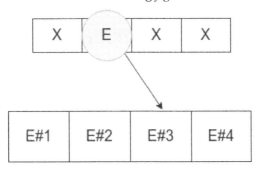

Figure 8.2: *Random Choice Mutation for Enumerated Gene Encoding*

Let's see the implementation of enumerated encoded genes ch8/enumerated_genes.py.

Individual is defined in the following way:

```
class EnumeratedIndividual:
    x_set = ['A', 'B', 'C', 'D']
    def __init__(self, gene_list):
        self.gene_list = gene_list
```

And genetic operation implementations:

```
def create_random():
```

```
    return EnumeratedIndividual([random.choice(EnumeratedIndividual.x_
set)])

def crossover(p1, p2):
    return EnumeratedIndividual([p2[0]]), EnumeratedIndividual([p1[0]])

def mutation(ind):
    return EnumeratedIndividual([random.choice(EnumeratedIndividual.x_
set)])
```

8.3 Genetic algorithm architecture

Let's build the GA architecture that uses the previously discussed approaches. Say we have to find the maxima of the following function:

```
import math

def complicated_one(a, b, x, n, fun_name):
    sum_ = 0
    for i in range(10, 10 + n + 1):
        if fun_name == 'cos':
            trig_value = math.cos(math.log2(b**n + 1) * math.pi * x) /\
                         (n + 1) + math.sin(x)**n
        elif fun_name == 'sin':
            trig_value = math.sin(math.log2(b**n + 1) * math.pi * x) /\
                         (n + 1) + math.cos(x)**n
        else:
            raise Exception(f'Unknown Function: {fun_name}')
        resid = trig_value - math.log2(n + 1)
        div = ((n + 1)**2) * (1 + a + b) * (120 - x**2) * resid + 1 / 2
        sum_ += ((x * n + math.log(n + 1)) / div) / (10**15)
    return sum_
```

where:

- a is real and $0 < a < 1$
- b is real and $0 < b < 1$
- x is real and $-10 < x < 10$
- n is natural and $n \le 20$
- fun_name is one of the functions: sin, cos

Well, as we can see, it is a rather tricky problem if you approach it analytically. Therefore, it is natural to treat this function as a black-box, and try to find the maxima or this function using a GA.

Let's study the GA implementation solving this issue ch8/ga.py.

We have the following type of genes:

- a,b,x – real-encoded genes
- n – discrete-encoded gene
- fun_name – enumerated-encoded gene

So, we have the following individual:

```
class Individual:
    counter = 0
    n_set = range(0, 21)
    func_set = ['sin', 'cos']

    def __init__(self, gene_list):
        self.__class__.counter += 1
        a_raw, b_raw, x_raw, n_raw, func_name = gene_list
        self.gene_list = [
            range_limit(a_raw, 0, 1),
            range_limit(b_raw, 0, 1),
            range_limit(x_raw, -100, 100),
            closest(n_raw, self.n_set),
            func_name
        ]

        a, b, x, n, func_name = self.gene_list
        self.fitness = complicated_one(a, b, x, n, func_name)
```

Creation of random individual:

```
def create_random():
    return Individual([
        random.uniform(0, 1),
        random.uniform(0, 1),
        random.uniform(-10, 10),
        random.choice(Individual.n_set),
        random.choice(Individual.func_set)
    ])
```

Since we have different types of genes in an individual, we need to determine the crossover and mutation for each gene separately. We will use crossover based on blend crossover, and mutation based on random deviation:

```python
def crossover(p1, p2):
    prob = .5
    a1, b1, x1, n1, func_name1 = copy.deepcopy(p1.gene_list)
    a2, b2, x2, n2, func_name2 = copy.deepcopy(p2.gene_list)

    if random.random() < prob:
        a1, a2 = crossover_blend(a1, a2, 0.3)

    if random.random() < prob:
        b1, b2 = crossover_blend(b1, b2, 0.5)

    if random.random() < prob:
        x1, x2 = crossover_blend(x1, x2, 1)

    if random.random() < prob:
        n1, n2 = crossover_blend(n1, n2, 0.5)

    if random.random() < prob:
        func_name1, func_name2 = func_name2, func_name1

    return Individual([a1, b1, x1, n1, func_name1]), Individual([a2, b2, x2, n2, func_name2])

def mutate(ind):
    prob = .5
    a, b, x, n, func_name = copy.deepcopy(ind.gene_list)
    if random.random() < prob:
        a = mutation_random_deviation(a, 0, .2, 1)

    if random.random() < prob:
        b = mutation_random_deviation(b, 0, .2, 1)

    if random.random() < prob:
        x = mutation_random_deviation(x, 0, 1, 1)

    if random.random() < prob:
        n = mutation_random_deviation(n, 0, 1, 1)
```

```
    if random.random() < prob:
        func_name = random.choice(Individual.func_set)

    return Individual([a, b, x, n, func_name])
```

For the research of the surface of multivariable and complicated functions, it is always better to use big populations and a large number of generations:

```
POPULATION_SIZE = 200
CROSSOVER_PROBABILITY = .8
MUTATION_PROBABILITY = .2
MAX_GENERATIONS = 1_000
```

So, we can construct the flow of our GA:

```
first_population = [create_random() for _ in range(POPULATION_SIZE)]
population = first_population.copy()
fitness_list = [ind.fitness for ind in population]
fit_avg = [sum(fitness_list) / len(population)]
fit_best = [max(fitness_list)]
fit_best_ever = [max(fitness_list + fit_best)]
best_ind = random.choice(first_population)

generation_number = 0

while generation_number < MAX_GENERATIONS:
    generation_number += 1
    offspring = selection_rank_with_elite(population, elite_size = 3)
    crossed_offspring = crossover_operation(offspring, crossover,
CROSSOVER_PROBABILITY)
    mutated_offspring = mutation_operation(crossed_offspring, mutate,
MUTATION_PROBABILITY)
    population = mutated_offspring.copy()

    best_ind, fit_avg, fit_best, fit_best_ever = stats(population, best_
ind, fit_avg, fit_best, fit_best_ever)

plot_stats(fit_avg, fit_best, fit_best_ever, "Genetic Algorithm Flow")

print(f'Maxima: {best_ind.fitness}')
print(f'Best Individual : {best_ind.gene_list}')
print(f'Number of Individuals: {Individual.counter}')
```

Result

```
Maxima: 1900.786558482193
Best Individual: [0.3371062330539034, 0, -10.953844488733237, 4, 'cos']
Number of Individuals: 200122
```

So, the solution is *(a=0.3371, b=0, x=-10.9538, n=4, fun_name=cos)*, which is a completely unpredictable solution. Initially, looking at the function, we can assume that the maxima will be reached at any of the boundary values, which means that at least one of the boundaries of the gene range would be present in the solution: *a=0* or *a=1, b=0 or b=1, x=-100 or x=100, n=0 or n=20*. But it is not so; the solution was found inside all gene ranges.

Let's take a look at the following *figure 8.3:*

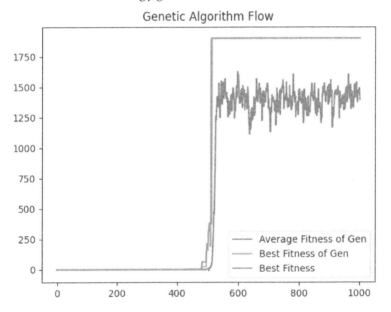

Figure 8.3: Genetic Algorithm Flow Statistics

Totally, about 200,000 individuals were generated, which means that the function was calculated about 200,000 times. This is not a large number exploring for a truly complicated function. Let's compare the GA performance with the brute force method. How close their results will be ch8/brute_force.py.

We will go through all gene ranges with a tiny step:

```
maximum = 0
counter = 0
ab_range = np.arange(0., 1., .02)
x_range = np.arange(-100, 101, .2)
```

```
n_range = range(0, 21)
fun_range = ['cos', 'sin']

total_iterations = len(ab_range) * len(ab_range) * len(x_range) \
                   * len(n_range) * len(fun_range)

for a in ab_range:
    for b in ab_range:
        for x in x_range:
            for n in n_range:
                for fun_name in fun_range:
                    counter += 1
                    val = complicated_one(a, b, x, n, fun_name)
                    if val > maximum:
                        maximum = val
                    if counter % 100_000 == 0:
                        print(f'processed iterations: {counter} '
                              f'from {total_iterations}')

print(f'Brute force maxima: {maximum} , counter: {counter}')
```

Result

Brute force maxima: 7.643536449503056e-11 , **counter:** 105525000

And what do we get here? The maxima value we found is 7.64e-11, the maxima is very close to zero, and we examined more than 100 million combinations! This example shows us that trying to find the maxima of a complex function by iterating over combinations of values does not lead to any result.

Conclusion

We have studied a very important aspect of the application of genetic algorithms. Finding the maxima of complex and difficult-to-analyze functions is a very common task. Of course, it should be kept in mind that genetic algorithms do not guarantee finding the global maxima, but nevertheless, they can be very useful when it is necessary to find any maxima in the foreseeable time. Such tasks are often encountered in the design of real-time systems. When the system may face the task of optimizing a completely unfamiliar function, it is necessary to find its maxima quickly.

In the next chapter, we will look at how genetic algorithms are used for combinatorial optimization.

Points to remember

- Black-box function is a function of complex nature, which we explore without diving into its nature.
- Before examining the function, you need to determine the range of input values.
- An individual usually uses one of the following types of gene encodings – real, discrete, enumeration.

Multiple choice questions

1. Let's say we have a function that takes the patient's blood group as a parameter. What gene encoding should we chose to represent blood group parameter?

    a) Real encoding

    b) Discrete encoding

    c) Enumeration encoding

2. Say we have discrete encoding on a set [-10, 0, 10]. We use the following function for mutation:

```
def closest(value, value_list):
    return min(value_list, key = lambda x: abs(x - value))

def mutate_random_deviation(x, mu = 0, sigma = 1):
    mutated_gene = mutate_random_deviation(x, mu, sigma)
    return closest(mutated_gene, [-10, 0, 10])
```

Will a gene with a value of 0 ever take on a value of 10 after mutation?

    a) Yes, theoretically it is possible

    b) No, that is impossible

Answers

1. c
2. a

Questions

1. What is the main difference between discrete encoding and enumeration encoding?

2. Try to find the maxima of the following function:

```python
import math

def some_function(op_major, op_minor, v1, v2):
    sign = math.copysign(1, op_minor)
    if op_major == 0:
        return v1 + abs(v2 - 15) - 100 * sign
    elif op_major == 1:
        return v1 * abs(v2 - 15) - 100 * sign
    elif op_major == 2:
        return pow(v1 + abs(v2 - 15), 3) - 100 * sign
    elif op_major == 3:
        return pow(v1 + abs(v2 - 15), 2) - 100 * sign
    elif op_major == 4:
        return 0,
    elif op_major == 5:
        return pow(v1 + abs(v2 - 15), 3) + 100 * sign
```

Key terms

- **Real encoding:** Gene is represented by value of float type.
- **Discrete encoding:** Gene is an element of a linear ordered finite set of values.
- **Enumeration encoding:** Gene is an element of enumeration set.

CHAPTER 9
Combinatorial Optimization – Binary Gene Encoding

In the last chapter, we studied how GAs can be applied to black-box functions, i.e., functions whose nature is completely unknown to us. Here we begin to consider the class of combinatorial optimization problems. In this class of problems, we know the nature of the problem a little more than the nature of the black-box function, which means we can build a more efficient scheme for finding a solution.

A combinatorial problem is a problem in which you need to find the best combination of some objects that gives the best result. Combinatorial optimization problems are often complicated to be solved analytically. Genetic algorithms are a very suitable method for solving combinatorial optimization problems. We will explore how GAs can solve problems without deep-diving into the specifics of the problem.

Let's consider the simplest example of a combinatorial optimization problem.

Suppose we have the following product list:

- Chocolate (546 calories)
- Tomato (20 calories)
- Apple (52 calories)
- Cookies (502 calories)
- Bread (265 calories)

And we need to choose the three lowest calorie items. The combination of these three products will be the solution to the combinatorial optimization problem. Combinatorial problems are usually much more complicated than the one we gave in the example. In this chapter, we will cover different combinatorial problems, the solution to which is a sequence of zeros or ones, and give intuition on how to solve them.

Structure

In this chapter, we will cover the following topics:

- Knapsack problem
- Schedule problem
- Radar placement problem

Objectives

The main objectives of this chapter are as follows:

- To give examples of combinatorial problems
- To understand how genetic algorithm solves them
- To define an architecture of genetic algorithm for combinatorial problems

9.1 Knapsack problem

The knapsack problem is a classic combinatorial optimization problem. The challenge is as follows – we have a knapsack with a capacity of 15kg, and we have many different items with different weights and costs. We have to select such things in a knapsack so that their price is maximum and, at the same time, does not exceed the capacity of the knapsack. Take a look at the following *figure 9.1:*

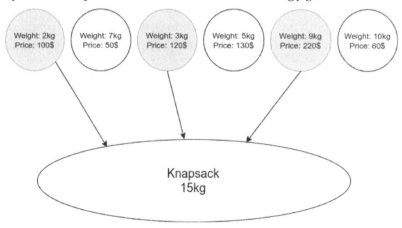

Figure 9.1: Knapsack Problem

Let's build a GA that solves this problem. For knapsack problem, the individual has the following binary gene set encoding:

- 1 - include item
- 0 - exclude item

Each individual represents a specific combination of things that should be put in a backpack. Fitness function is the total value of all items that are included in the combination. Let's take a look at the following *figure 9.2:*

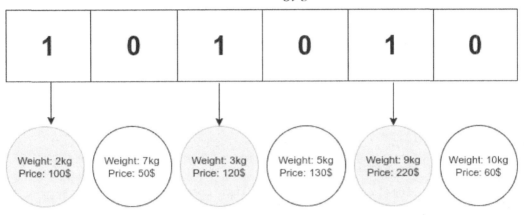

Figure 9.2: *Individual Representation for Knapsack Problem*

An individual for this problem can be described as follows: `ch9/knapsack/individual.py`:

Item definition

```
class Item:

    def __init__(self, name, weight, price) -> None:
        self.name = name
        self.weight = weight
        self.price = price
```

Structure of an individual for knapsack problem

```
class Individual:
    counter = 0

    @classmethod
    def set_items(cls, items):
        cls.items = items

    @classmethod
```

```python
    def set_max_weight(cls, max_weight):
        cls.max_weight = max_weight

    @classmethod
    def create_random(cls):
        return Individual([random.choice([0, 1]) for _ in range(len(cls.
items))])

    def __init__(self, gene_list) -> None:
        self.gene_list = gene_list
        self.fitness = self.fitness_function()
        self.__class__.counter += 1

    def total_price(self):
        return sum([i.price for i in list(compress(self.__class__.items,
self.gene_list))])

    def total_weight(self):
        return sum([i.weight for i in list(compress(self.__class__.
items, self.gene_list))])

    def fitness_function(self):
        if self.total_weight() > self.__class__.max_weight:
            return 0
        else:
            return self.total_price()

    def __str__(self):
        return f'gene: {self.gene_list}, price: {self.total_price()},
weight: {self.total_weight()}'

    def plot_info(self):
        print(f'Included: {[i.name for i in list(compress(self.__
class__.items, self.gene_list))]}')
        print(f'Fitness: {self.fitness}')
        print(f'Price: {self.total_price()}')
        print(f'Weight: {self.total_weight()}')
```

Generating random solution for a knapsack problem

```python
if __name__ == '__main__':

    random.seed(13)

    items = [
        Item('laptop', 3, 300),
        Item('book', 2, 15),
        Item('radio', 1, 30),
        Item('tv', 6, 230),
        Item('potato', 5, 7),
        Item('brick', 3, 1),
        Item('bottle', 1, 2),
        Item('camera', 0.5, 280),
        Item('smartphone', 0.1, 500),
        Item('picture', 1, 170),
        Item('flower', 2, 5),
        Item('chair', 3, 4),
        Item('watch', 0.05, 500),
        Item('boots', 1.5, 30),
        Item('radiator', 5, 25),
        Item('tablet', 0.5, 450),
        Item('printer', 4.5, 170)
    ]

    Individual.set_items(items)
    Individual.set_max_weight(10)

    ind = Individual.create_random()

    ind.plot_info()
```

Result

```
Included: ['laptop', 'book', 'flower', 'watch', 'tablet']
Fitness: 1270
Price: 1270
Weight: 7.55
```

Let's design an architecture, and test GA solving knapsack problem. Refer to the following *figure 9.3*:

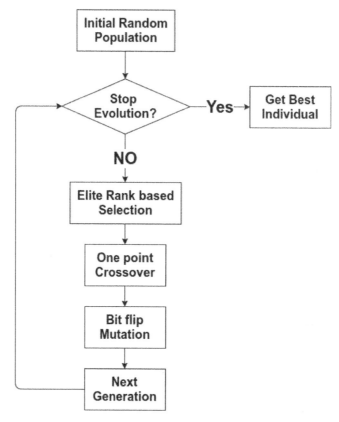

Figure 9.3: *Genetic Algorithm Design solving Knapsack Problem*

Say we have the following list of items in our room, and we want to take the most valuable things in case of escape:

- **Laptop:** 3kg, 300$
- **Book:** 2kg, 15$
- **Radio:** 1kg, 30$
- **TV:** 6kg, 230$
- **Potato:** 5kg, 7$
- **Brick:** 3kg, 1$
- **Bottle:** 1kg, 2$
- **Camera:** 0.5kg, 280$
- **Smartphone:** 0.1kg, 500$
- **Picture:** 1kg, 170$

- **Flower:** 2kg, 5$
- **Chair:** 3kg, 4$
- **Watch:** 0.05kg, 500$
- **Boots:** 1.5kg, 30$
- **Radiator:** 5kg, 25$
- **Tablet:** 0.5kg, 450$
- **Printer:** 4.5kg, 170$

Let's start building an algorithm that solves this problem `ch9/knapsack/ga_intuitive_approach.py`:

One point crossover and bit flip mutation

```
def crossover(parent1, parent2):
    child1_genes, child2_genes = crossover_one_point(parent1.gene_list,
parent2.gene_list)
    return Individual(child1_genes), Individual(child2_genes)


def mutate(ind):
    mutated_gene = mutation_bit_flip(ind.gene_list)
    return Individual(mutated_gene)
```

Settings of knapsack problem

```
Individual.set_items(get_items_from_my_room())
Individual.set_max_weight(10)
```

GA parameters

```
POPULATION_SIZE = 8
CROSSOVER_PROBABILITY = .7
MUTATION_PROBABILITY = .2
MAX_GENERATIONS = 20
```

Running GA

```
first_population = [Individual.create_random() for _ in range(POPULATION_
SIZE)]
population = first_population.copy()
fitness_list = [ind.fitness for ind in population]
fit_avg = [sum(fitness_list) / len(population)]
fit_best = [max(fitness_list)]
fit_best_ever = [max(fitness_list + fit_best)]
```

```
best_ind = random.choice(first_population)
population = first_population.copy()

generation_number = 0

while generation_number < MAX_GENERATIONS:
    generation_number += 1
    offspring = selection_rank_with_elite(population, elite_size = 2)
    crossed_offspring = crossover_operation(offspring, crossover,
CROSSOVER_PROBABILITY)
    mutated_offspring = mutation_operation(crossed_offspring, mutate,
MUTATION_PROBABILITY)
    population = mutated_offspring.copy()

    best_ind, fit_avg, fit_best, fit_best_ever = stats(population, best_
ind, fit_avg, fit_best, fit_best_ever)

plot_stats(fit_avg, fit_best_ever, "Knapsack Problem")
best_ind.plot_info()
```

Result

Included: ['laptop', 'radio', 'bottle', 'camera', 'smartphone',
'picture', 'flower', 'watch', 'tablet']

Fitness: 2237

Price: 2237

Weight: 9.15

And our evolution progress looks like the following *figure 9.4:*

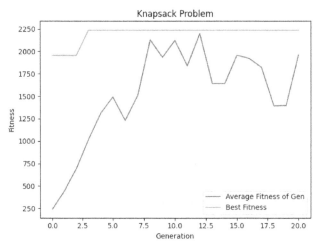

Figure 9.4: *Solving Knapsack Problem Evolution Progress*

This task does not seem so tricky, but consider a more general problem when the number of items is much larger. Let's make a generator of such a set `ch9/knapsack/random_set_generator.py`:

```
import random
import matplotlib.pyplot as plt

from ch9.knapsack.individual import Item

def random_set_generator(min_price, max_price, min_weight, max_weight,
total_number):
    l = []
    for i in range(total_number):
        l.append(Item(f'Item#{i}', random.uniform(min_weight, max_
weight), random.uniform(min_price, max_price)))
    return l

if __name__ == '__main__':
    random.seed(15)
    items = random_set_generator(1, 100, 0.1, 7, 200)
    plt.scatter([i.weight for i in items], [i.price for i in items])
    plt.xlabel('weight')
    plt.ylabel('price')
    plt.show()
```

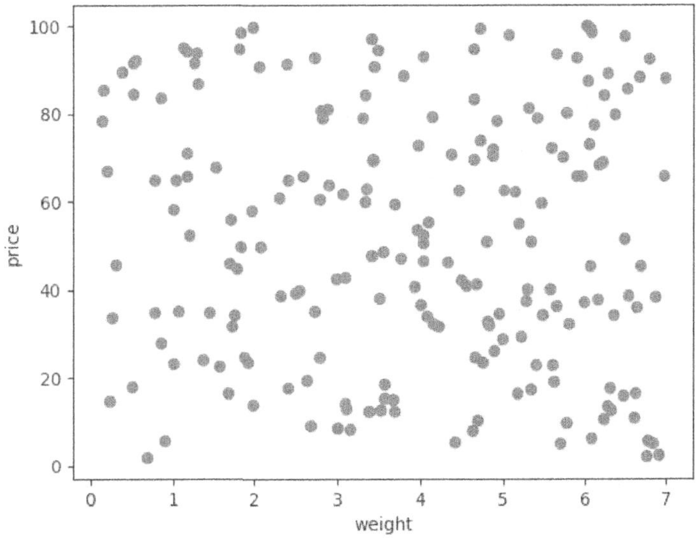

Figure 9.5: Random Set of Items

In the preceding *figure 9.5,* we have 200 items, or 2200 possible combinations. This number is comparable to the number of planets in the universe.

But before we dive into this general problem, let's look at our function for generating a random individual. A random individual is generated as a random set of zeros and ones. Let's see what the average weight will be for our random individual for a random set of 200 items, `ch9/knapsack/random_individual.py`:

```python
import random

from ch9.knapsack.individual import Individual
from ch9.knapsack.random_set_generator import random_set_generator

if __name__ == '__main__':
    random.seed(1)

    items = random_set_generator(1, 100, 0.1, 7, 200)
    Individual.set_items(items)
    Individual.set_max_weight(10)

    population = [Individual.create_random() for _ in range(1000)]
    average_weight = sum([ind.total_weight() for ind in population]) / len(population)
    print(f'Average weight of population: {average_weight}')
```

Result

Average weight of population: 356.26

If we solve the problem for a 10kg knapsack, then with an average initial random individual of 350 kg, it will take us a lot more time to come up with at least some solution. This will happen because initially, almost all individuals will be unviable, and have a fitness function equal to 0. It will take a lot of time and generations before a population appears with an average weight of an individual less than 10. Therefore, what we can do is shift the balance of zeros and ones in the genes of randomly generated individuals, so that there are many more zeros, `ch9/knapsack/random_individual_shifted_zeros.py`:

```python
import random

from ch9.knapsack.individual import Individual
from ch9.knapsack.random_set_generator import random_set_generator

def create_random_individual(gene_len, zeros = 1, ones = 1):
    s = ([0] * zeros) + ([1] * ones)
    return Individual([random.choice(s) for _ in range(gene_len)])
```

```
if __name__ == '__main__':
    random.seed(1)

    items = random_set_generator(1, 100, 0.1, 7, 200)
    Individual.set_items(items)
    Individual.set_max_weight(10)

    population = [create_random_individual(len(items), 50, 1) for _ in
range(1000)]
    average_weight = sum([ind.total_weight() for ind in population]) /
len(population)
    print(f'Average weight of population: {average_weight}')
```

Result

Average weight of population: 13.85

This approach is much more suitable, and is going to be a good starting population for GA, `ch9/knapsack/ga_general.py`.

Result

Best Fitness: 802.37

Total Number of Individuals: 9169

Let's take a look at the following *figure 9.6:*

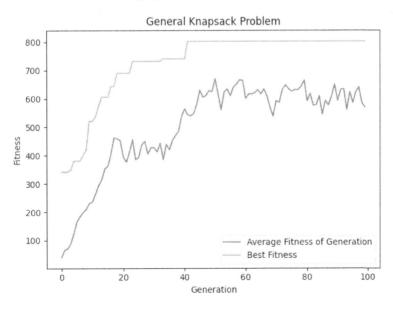

Figure 9.6: Solving General Knapsack Problem

Well, not bad, but there is one more improvement in our algorithm. As you can see, any individual who is close to maximum capacity can be destroyed very easily. The addition of any inappropriate item can set fitness function to zero. To check this hypothesis, we will take the best individual from the previous example, and make 1000 mutations on it, and then will check how many mutations have killed the best individual, ch9/knapsack/individual_mutation.py:

```python
import random
import matplotlib.pyplot as plt
from ch9.knapsack.individual import Individual
from ch9.knapsack.random_set_generator import random_set_generator
from ch9.knapsack.toolbox import mutation_bit_flip

def mutate(ind):
    mutated_gene = mutation_bit_flip(ind.gene_list)
    return Individual(mutated_gene)

if __name__ == '__main__':
    random.seed(1)

    random.seed(63)

    items = random_set_generator(1, 100, 0.1, 7, 200)
    Individual.set_items(items)
    Individual.set_max_weight(10)

    gene_set = [0] * len(items)
    inclusions = [2, 30, 34, 42, 48, 64, 85, 104, 113, 119, 157, 174]
    for i in inclusions:
        gene_set[i] = 1
    ind = Individual(gene_set)

    alive = 0
    killed = 0

    for _ in range(1000):
        mutated = mutate(ind)
        if mutated.fitness == 0:
            killed += 1
        else:
            alive += 1
```

```
print(f'Best individual: {ind.fitness}')
labels = 'Killed', 'Alive'
sizes = [killed, alive]
plt.pie(sizes, labels = labels)
plt.show ()
```

Result

Best individual 802.3740868900151

Let's take a look at the following *figure 9.7:*

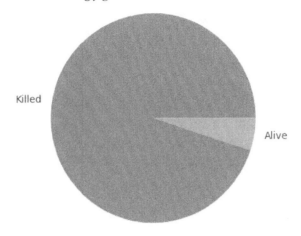

Figure 9.7: *Results of Bit Flip Mutation of Best Individual*

Only 5% of mutations keep the best individual alive. The rest of the mutations kill the individual, thereby excluding it from the population, and thereby erasing all the useful information that this individual carried. It is not difficult to conclude that a similar situation occurs with crossover. Any crossing is capable of producing non-viable offspring.

> **NOTE: The feature of fast destructibility of individuals is natural in all discrete optimization problems. It is obvious that a change in one value of one gene can completely change the value of a fitness function.**

Let's change our GA architecture:

- From one-point crossover to fitness driven one-point crossover
- From bit flip mutation to fitness driven bit flip mutation

What we did was to protect individuals from unsuccessful crossings and mutations. Let's see the performance of our algorithm after the changes made, `ch9/knapsack/ ga_general_fitness_driven.py`:

Fitness driven one-point crossover, fitness driven bit flip mutation and elite rank selection:

```python
def crossover(parent1, parent2):
    return crossover_fitness_driven_one_point(parent1, parent2)

def mutate(ind):
    return mutation_fitness_driven_bit_flip(ind, max_tries = 3)

def select(population):
    return selection_rank_with_elite(population, elite_size = 2)
```

Inputs for knapsack problem

```python
items = random_set_generator(1, 100, 0.1, 7, 200)
Individual.set_items(items)
Individual.set_max_weight(10)
```

GA parameters

```python
POPULATION_SIZE = 100
CROSSOVER_PROBABILITY = .7
MUTATION_PROBABILITY = .2
MAX_GENERATIONS = 50
```

GA implementation

```python
first_population = [create_random_individual(len(items), zeros = 30) for
_ in range(POPULATION_SIZE)]
population = first_population.copy()
fitness_list = [ind.fitness for ind in population]
fit_avg = [sum(fitness_list) / len(population)]
fit_best = [max(fitness_list)]
fit_best_ever = [max(fitness_list + fit_best)]
best_ind = random.choice(first_population)

generation_number = 0

while generation_number < MAX_GENERATIONS:
    generation_number += 1
    offspring = select(population)
    crossed_offspring = crossover_operation(offspring, crossover,
CROSSOVER_PROBABILITY)
    mutated_offspring = mutation_operation(crossed_offspring, mutate,
```

```
MUTATION_PROBABILITY)
    population = mutated_offspring.copy()

    best_ind, fit_avg, fit_best, fit_best_ever = stats(population, best_
ind, fit_avg, fit_best, fit_best_ever)

plot_stats(fit_avg, fit_best_ever, "General Knapsack Problem")
print(f'Best Fitness: {best_ind.fitness}')
print(f'Total Number of Individuals: {Individual.counter}')
```

Result

Best Fitness: 1166.73

Total Number of Individuals: 6479

Let's take a look at the following *figure 9.8:*

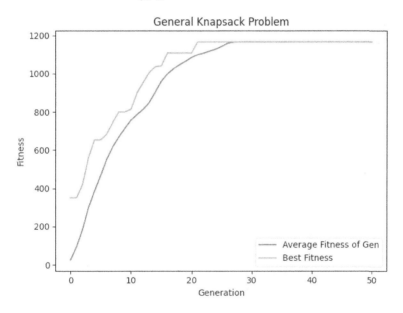

Figure 9.8: *Improved Fitness Driven Genetic Algorithm*

As we can see, this architecture converges to the solution faster, and the fitness function of the solution is higher than that of the previous architecture.

But of course, we understand that one architecture test cannot be a reliable proof for one architecture being better than another. Compare two different architectures using the Monte-Carlo simulation method. Simulations – `ch9/knapsack/ga_general_fitness_driven_montecarlo.py`, `ch9/knapsack/ga_general_montecarlo.py` gives us the result:

Algorithm #1, as shown in the following *figure 9.9:*

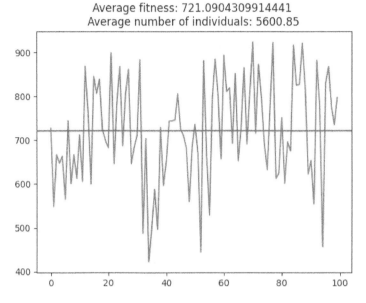

Figure 9.9: *Monte-Carlo Simulation of initial Genetic Algorithm Architecture.*

Algorithm #2, as shown in the following *figure 9.10:*

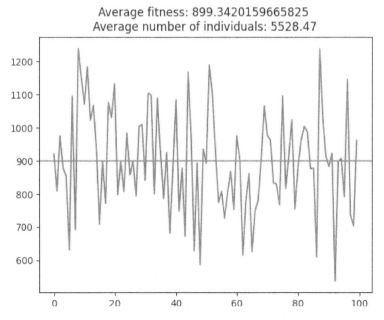

Figure 9.10: *Monte-Carlo Simulation of improved Genetic Algorithm Architecture with Fitness Driven Crossover and Mutation.*

As we expected, the improved version of the GA gives a 25% better fitness result for the same number of individuals.

The knapsack problem can be easily extended for more sophisticated problems and conditions. For example, if we need to compose the most nutritious diet for a certain amount of money, and diet should include a certain amount of proteins, fats and carbohydrates, then we will have three more boundary conditions in addition to the condition for the cost of products, which is similar to the capacity condition in the knapsack problem.

9.2 Schedule problem

Another combinatorial optimization problem that we will study is the schedule problem. In this task, there is a certain number of workers and requirements for their work schedule; it is necessary to select a work schedule that will satisfy all the requirements.

Here is an example of a schedule with the following inputs (refer to the following *figure 9.11*):

- 7 working days
- 4 workers
- A worker cannot work for more than two days in a row
- One worker only works on Sundays

	Mon	Tue	Wen	Thu	Fri	Sat	Sun
Emp 1	X		X	X		X	
Emp 2	X	X		X	X		
Emp 3		X	X		X	X	
Emp 4							X

Figure 9.11: Schedule

This schedule is not difficult to construct. But let's look at more complex conditions:

- 7 working days and 3 shifts per day – morning, midday, and evening shift
- 5 workers
- In the morning, there should be at least 1, and maximum 4 workers
- In the midday, there should be at least 2, and maximum 5 workers
- In the evening, there must be at least 1, and maximum 2 workers

- After the morning and afternoon shifts, the worker must rest for at least one shift, that is, one cannot work in a row, morning and afternoon, or day and evening
- After the evening shift, the worker must rest for a day, that is, not work on any of the next day's shifts

Well, this problem is no longer so easy to solve. There are more than 2100 different schedule variations, and it is clear that we cannot solve this problem by brute force.

NOTE: At this point, you can stop and try to build an individual binary gene encoding, which will represent some schedule view. This will be a very useful exercise.

The binary construction of day shifts for an employee can be represented as shown in the following *figure 9.12*:

Figure 9.12: Shift Binary Representation

So, the whole schedule for one worker can be represented in such a way (refer to the following *figure 9.13*):

1, 0, 0   0, 0, 1   1, 1,0   0,0,0   0, 1, 0   1, 0, 0   1, 0, 0

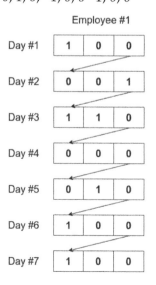

Figure 9.13: Schedule for One Worker

And the whole schedule for all workers can be represented as shown in the following *figure 9.14:*

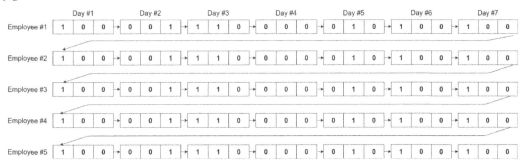

Figure 9.14: *Binary Representation of Whole Schedule*

So, we see that the schedule can be represented as a sequence of 105 ones and zeros. Let's look at the implementation of an individual that realizes the work schedule model, ch9/schedule/individual.py.

Definition of the individual class for a schedule problem

```
class Individual:
    counter = 0
    period = 0
    employees = 0

    @classmethod
    def set_fitness_function(cls, fun):
        cls.fitness_function = fun

    @classmethod
    def set_period(cls, period):
        cls.period = period

    @classmethod
    def set_employees(cls, employees):
        cls.employees = employees

    @classmethod
    def generate_random(cls):
        return Individual([random.choice([0, 1]) for _ in range(cls.
period * cls.employees * 3)])
```

```python
    def __init__(self, gene_list) -> None:
        self.gene_list = gene_list
        self.fitness = self.__class__.fitness_function(self.create_
schedule())

    def create_schedule(self):
        t = {}
        for e in range(1, self.employees + 1):
            shift_len = 3 * self.period
            t[e] = self.gene_list[shift_len * (e - 1): shift_len * e]
        schedule_df = pd.DataFrame(data = t)
        return schedule_df

    def plot_schedule(self):
        schedule_df = self.create_schedule()
        x_labels = []
        shift_names = {0: 'mor', 1: 'mid', 2: 'evn'}
        for i in range(0, 3 * self.period):
            day = floor(i / 3) + 1
            shift = shift_names[i % 3]
            x_labels.append(f'Day {day} : {shift}')
        plt.xticks(list(range(0, 3 * self.period)), x_labels, rotation =
90)
        y_labels = []
        for i in range(0, self.employees):
            y_labels.append(f'Emp: {i+1}')
        plt.yticks(list(range(0, self.employees)), y_labels)
        plt.imshow(schedule_df.T, cmap = 'binary')
        plt.title(f'Fitness: {self.fitness}')
        plt.show()
```

Generating random individual with plot

```python
if __name__ == '__main__':

    Individual.set_employees(5)
    Individual.set_period(7)

    def fitness_function(df):
        return 0
```

```
Individual.set_fitness_function(fitness_function)

ind = Individual.generate_random()
ind.plot_schedule()
```

Take a look at the following *figure 9.15:*

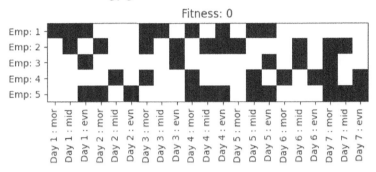

Figure 9.15: *Random Individual Representing Schedule*

And so, we have determined the binary structure of the working schedule, and implemented the genotype of the individual population. But now the questions arise – What will be the fitness function for the individual? How to compare two individuals and understand that one of them is better than the other?

To solve this problem, we will take the following approach. We will calculate the penalty points for each graph. The more violations and deviations from the rules that the schedule contains, the more penalty points it will be awarded. According to this logic, an individual with a fitness function equal to 0 will be the solution to our problem.

> **NOTE: Obviously, the schedule problem contains quite a lot of solutions. Only one representative of this set has to be found.**

A schematic of an evolutionary search might look like as shown in the following *figure 9.16:*

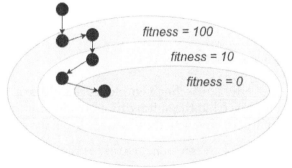

Figure 9.16: *Genetic Algorithm Search for Schedule Problem*

First condition – minimum and maximum presence. We have to impose minimum and maximum shift attendance conditions. If we have a maximum of two employees in the evening, and the schedule indicates 4, then the schedule receives two penalty points. And we will add the condition that the absence of anyone on the shift is completely unacceptable, and we will immediately add 100 penalty points in case of such an event, ch9/schedule/schedule_analyzer.py:

```python
def shift_deviations(df, mor_min, mor_max, day_min, day_max, evn_min,
evn_max):
    min_mor_dev = 0
    max_mor_dev = 0
    min_day_dev = 0
    max_day_dev = 0
    min_evn_dev = 0
    max_evn_dev = 0
    empty_penalty = 0
    for i in range(0, len(df)):
        shift_ord = i % 3
        empl_per_shift = df.sum(axis = 1)[i]
        if shift_ord == 0:
            min_mor_dev += max(mor_min - empl_per_shift, 0)
            max_mor_dev += max(empl_per_shift - mor_max, 0)
        elif shift_ord == 1:
            min_day_dev += max(day_min - empl_per_shift, 0)
            max_day_dev += max(empl_per_shift - day_max, 0)
        elif shift_ord == 2:
            min_evn_dev += max(evn_min - empl_per_shift, 0)
            max_evn_dev += max(empl_per_shift - evn_max, 0)
        if empl_per_shift == 0:
            empty_penalty += 100

    return min_mor_dev + max_mor_dev + min_day_dev + max_day_dev + min_
evn_dev + max_evn_dev + empty_penalty
```

Second condition – rest after shifts. Each employee should rest for the allotted time after the shift. If the employee left the shift without resting for the allotted time, then one penalty point is charged, ch9/schedule/schedule_analyzer.py:

```python
def shift_relax(df, relax_after_mon, relax_after_day, relax_after_evn):
    violations = 0
```

```
for e in range(0, len(df.columns)):
    relax_counter = 0
    for s in range(0, len(df)):
        shift = df.iloc[s, e]
        if shift == 1:
            if relax_counter > 0:
                violations += 1
            shift_order = s % 3
            if shift_order == 0:
                relax_counter = relax_after_mon
            elif shift_order == 1:
                relax_counter = relax_after_day
            elif shift_order == 2:
                relax_counter = relax_after_evn
        else:
            relax_counter = max(0, relax_counter - 1)
return violations
```

Let us assume that violation of labor standards is much worse than incomplete staffing of a shift. Penalty points that an individual received for the lack of an individual are much more significant than penalty points for the rules of attendance shift. Then:

fitness function = - (5 × rest penalty + presence penalty)

As we have already noticed, the schedule problem differs from others such that we can definitely understand that we have found the best solution. In the problems that we studied before, the probability of finding a better solution remained for each generation. But here, in the case of finding an individual with a fitness function equal to 0, we can immediately stop the search; so we will add this stop condition to the architecture of our algorithm.

Take a look at the following *figure 9.17*:

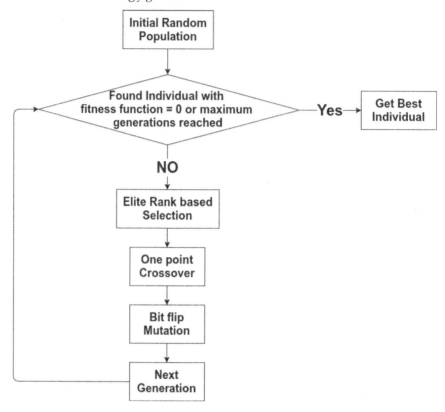

Figure 9.17: *Genetic Algorithm Architecture for Schedule Problem*

Here is the GA implementation, `ch9/schedule/ga_schedule.py`:

3-point crossover, bit flip mutation, and rank selection with elite:

```
def crossover(parent1, parent2):
    child1_genes, child2_genes = crossover_n_point(parent1.gene_list,
parent2.gene_list, 3)
    return Individual(child1_genes), Individual(child2_genes)


def mutate(ind):
    mutated_gene = mutation_bit_flip(ind.gene_list)
    return Individual(mutated_gene)


def select(population):
    return selection_rank_with_elite(population, elite_size = 2)
```

Settings of schedule problem

- 5 employees
- 7 day cycle

```
Individual.set_employees(5)

Individual.set_period(7)
```

Fitness function

- Minimum 1 and maximum 4 per morning
- Minimum 2 and maximum 5 per midday
- Minimum 1 and maximum 2 per evening
- Relax 1 shift after morning work shift
- Relax 1 shift after midday work shift
- Relax 3 shift after evening work shift

```
def fitness_function(df):
    dev = shift_deviations(df,
                     mor_min = 1, mor_max = 4,
                     day_min = 2, day_max = 5,
                     evn_min = 1, evn_max = 2
                     )
    relax = shift_relax(df, 1, 1, 3)
    return -(dev + relax * 5)


Individual.set_fitness_function(fitness_function)
```

GA parameters

```
POPULATION_SIZE = 30
CROSSOVER_PROBABILITY = .8
MUTATION_PROBABILITY = .5
MAX_GENERATIONS = 200
```

GA implementation

```
first_population = [Individual.generate_random() for _ in
range(POPULATION_SIZE)]
best_ind = random.choice(first_population)
fit_avg = []
fit_best = []
generation_num = 0
```

```
population = first_population.copy()

while generation_num < MAX_GENERATIONS and best_ind.fitness != 0:
    generation_num += 1
    offspring = select(population)
    crossed_offspring = crossover_operation(offspring, crossover,
CROSSOVER_PROBABILITY)
    mutated_offspring = mutation_operation(crossed_offspring,
mutate, MUTATION_PROBABILITY)
    population = mutated_offspring.copy()
    best_ind, fit_avg, fit_best = stats(population, best_ind, fit_avg,
fit_best)

plot_stats(fit_avg, fit_best, "Schedule Problem")

print(f'Total Number of Individuals: {Individual.counter}')
best_ind.plot_schedule()
```

Result

Total Number of Individuals: 4968

Let's take a look at the following *figure 9.18:*

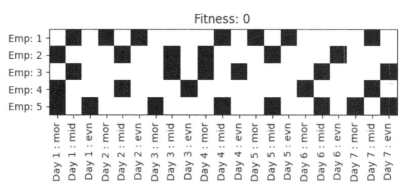

Figure 9.18: *Solution of Schedule Problem*

And we can see dynamics of population evolution in the following *figure 9.19*:

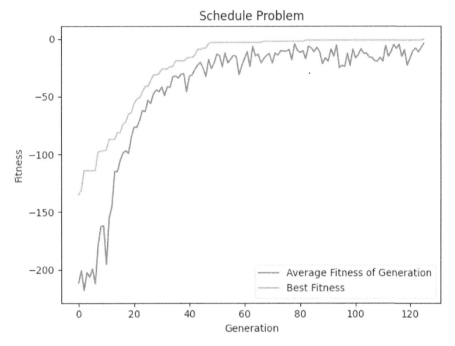

Figure 9.19: *Genetic Algorithm Statistics*

As you can see in the preceding *figure 9.19*, at the beginning, the algorithm converges quite quickly, but it spends quite a lot of time to overcome the last step.

Congratulations! We have built a general mechanism for solving a very complex problem. As you can see from the implementation, we can choose any number of employees, the duration of the work cycle, rest restrictions, and so on. We can also add different conditions, such as different shift wages for workers, and minimize costs when drawing up a work schedule.

9.3 Radar placement problem

Let's consider the next problem now. We have a map of the land surface. This map will be divided into squares. On this map, there are square types – river, lake, meadow, hill, city. We need to place some radars on this map that will cover all the cities.

Take a look at the following *figure 9.20:*

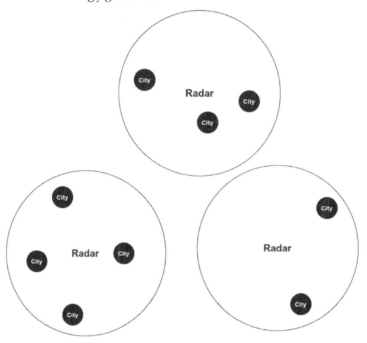

Figure 9.20: *Radar Placement*

Of course, this task has a trivial solution; just put a radar on every square on the map. This way, we are guaranteed to cover all cities. Although naturally, such a solution is unacceptable. Radars are very expensive, and they consume a lot of resources, which need to be maintained. Therefore, it is natural to add the condition that the number of radars covering all cities should be minimal.

Now, let's take a look at the following *figure 9.21:*

31$	39$	25$	50$	105$
29$	132$	231$	35$	59$
51$	City	511$	23$	45$
34$	213$	480$	City	63$
11$	33$	113$	45$	35$

Figure 9.21: *Radar Placement Costs on each square*

For a really large map with a lot of squares and cities, this is quite a computational challenge. A 100 by 100 map formally has 210000 solutions. Of course, this problem cannot be solved by brute force search.

Refer to the following *figure 9.22* for an example of map 50x50:

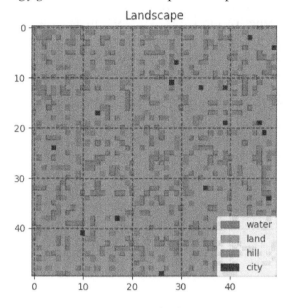

Figure 9.22: *Example of map 50×50*

An example of a map of cities and radar coverage can be plotted as shown in the following *figure 9.23:*

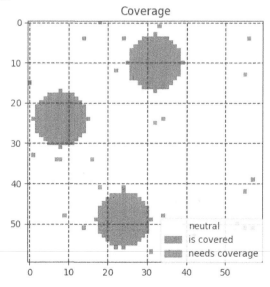

Figure 9.23: *Cities and Radars*

> NOTE: This problem, formulated in a general way, has great practical interest – placement of cell towers, supply centers, air security points, mineral mining, and so on. For example, suppose we have a flying robot that will take soil samples from an unknown planet. This robot has a limited number of landings, and we need to cover the area of the most valuable resources in the minimum number of landings. The task of taking soil samples for the robot is reduced to the task of placing radars. There is no analytical solution for this class of problems, and they must be solved rather quickly. The use of GAs is the optimal tool for finding solutions.

So, how will the solution of our problem be presented, and what will an individual of the population of the GA be like? The solution will obviously be a map with squares where the radars should be placed. Therefore, the individual will have binary encoded genes, as shown in the following *figure 9.24:*

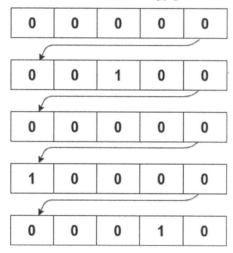

Figure 9.24: Binary Encoding for Radar Placement on 5×5 map

Individual solving this problem will already have a familiar structure, ch9/radar/ individual.py.

Individual

```
class Individual:
    counter = 0
    rows = 0
    cols = 0

    @classmethod
    def set_fitness_function(cls, fun):
        cls.fitness_function = fun
```

```python
    @classmethod
    def generate_random(cls, radar_prob):
        gene_list = [0] * cls.rows * cls.cols
        for i in range(cls.rows * cls.cols):
            if random.random() < radar_prob:
                gene_list[i] = 1
        return Individual(gene_list)

    def __init__(self, gene_list) -> None:
        self.gene_list = gene_list
        self.fitness = self.__class__.fitness_function(self.get_
coordinates())
        self.__class__.counter += 1

    def get_coordinates(self):
        r = self.__class__.rows
        c = self.__class__.cols
        matrix = [[None] * c for _ in range(r)]
        for i in range(r):
            for j in range(c):
                matrix[i][j] = self.gene_list[i * r + j]
        return matrix

    def count_radars(self):
        return sum(self.gene_list)
```

Generation of random individual

```python
Individual.rows = 50
Individual.cols = 50


# fintess function undefined yet
def fintess_function(coords):
    return 0


Individual.set_fitness_function(fintess_function)
ind = Individual.generate_random(.01)
```

Let's explore the generation of a random landscape map, `ch9/radar/landscape.py`.

Let us have the following types of surfaces:
```
class SquareType(Enum):
    water = auto()
    land = auto()
    hill = auto()
    city = auto()
```

The map is a matrix of squares. A square is defined as follows:

```
class Square:

    def __init__(self, type, needs_coverage, tower_cost, is_covered = False):
        self.type = type
        self.needs_coverage = needs_coverage
        self.is_covered = is_covered
        self.tower_cost = tower_cost
        self.has_radar = False
```

And we create separate class for landscape map:
```
class Landscape:

    def __init__(self, matrix):
        self.matrix = matrix

    def rows(self):
        return len(self.matrix)

    def cols(self):
        return len(self.matrix[0])
```

Generation of random landscape:
```
def generate_random_landscape(points, weights, rows, cols):
    matrix = [[None] * cols for _ in range(rows)]
    for i in range(rows):
        for j in range(cols):
            p = random.choices(points, weights.values())
            square = copy.deepcopy(p[0])
```

```
            square.tower_cost = round(square.tower_cost * (1 + random.
uniform(0, .1)))
            matrix[i][j] = square
    return Landscape(matrix)
```

Let's create some plotting functions. Landscape plot:

```
def plot_landscape(landscape):
    square_colors = {
        SquareType.water: 1,
        SquareType.land:  11,
        SquareType.hill:  21,
        SquareType.city:  31
    }
    m = np.empty([landscape.rows(), landscape.cols()])
    for i in range(landscape.rows()):
        for j in range(landscape.cols()):
            m[i, j] = square_colors[landscape.matrix[i][j].type]
    col_list = ['blue', 'green', 'brown', 'black']
    labels = [s.name for s in square_colors.keys()]
    cmap = colors.ListedColormap(col_list)
    bounds = [0, 10, 20, 30, 40]
    norm = colors.BoundaryNorm(bounds, cmap.N)

    plt.imshow(m, cmap = cmap, norm = norm)
    plt.grid(which = 'major', axis = 'both', linestyle = '--', color =
'k', linewidth = 1)
    patches = [mpatches.Patch(color = col_list[i], label = labels[i])
for i in range(len(col_list))]
    plt.legend(handles = patches, loc = 4, borderaxespad = 0.)
    plt.title('Landscape')
    plt.show()
```

Coverage plot:

```
def plot_coverage(landscape, title = "Coverage"):
    coverage_colors = {
        'neutral':         1,
        'is covered':      11,
        'needs coverage': 21
```

```
    }

    m = np.empty([landscape.rows(), landscape.cols()])
    for i in range(landscape.rows()):
        for j in range(landscape.cols()):
            if landscape.matrix[i][j].is_covered:
                m[i, j] = coverage_colors['is covered']
            elif not landscape.matrix[i][j].needs_coverage:
                m[i, j] = coverage_colors['neutral']
            elif landscape.matrix[i][j].needs_coverage:
                m[i, j] = coverage_colors['needs coverage']

    col_list = ['white', 'green', 'red']
    labels = list(coverage_colors.keys())
    cmap = colors.ListedColormap(col_list)
    bounds = [0, 10, 20, 30]
    norm = colors.BoundaryNorm(bounds, cmap.N)

    plt.imshow(m, cmap = cmap, norm = norm)
    plt.grid(which = 'major', axis = 'both', linestyle = '--', color =
'k', linewidth = 1)
    patches = [mpatches.Patch(color = col_list[i], label = labels[i])
for i in range(len(col_list))]
    plt.legend(handles = patches, loc = 4, borderaxespad = 0.)
    plt.title('Coverage')
    plt.show()
```

Plot costs of radar construction on each square:

```
def plot_costs(landscape):
    m = np.empty([landscape.rows(), landscape.cols()])
    for i in range(landscape.rows()):
    for j in range(landscape.cols()):

        m[i, j] = landscape.matrix[i][j].tower_cost

    plt.imshow(m, cmap = cm.Reds)
    plt.colorbar()
    plt.title('Radar Construction Costs')
    plt.show()
```

Now we are ready to generate a random landscape map, and a random individual, and apply this individual to the map.

Map size 60×60 :

```
rows = 60
cols = 60
```

Type of squares, and their probability weights appearing on the map:

```
square_grid = {
    Square(SquareType.water, needs_coverage = False, tower_cost = 500): 20,
    Square(SquareType.land, needs_coverage = False, tower_cost = 30):  100,
    Square(SquareType.hill, needs_coverage = False, tower_cost = 100): 8,
    Square(SquareType.city, needs_coverage = True, tower_cost = 200):  1
}
```

Generating random landscape:

```
landscape = generate_random_landscape(list(square_grid.keys()), square_grid, rows, cols)
```

Plotting landscape:

```
plot_landscape(landscape)

plot_costs(landscape)

plot_coverage(landscape)
```

Generating random individual:

```
def fintess_function(coords):
    return 0

Individual.set_fitness_function(fintess_function)
Individual.rows = rows
Individual.cols = cols
ind = Individual.generate_random(.0005)
```

Applying random individual to landscape:

```
test_landscape = copy.deepcopy(landscape)
test_landscape.add_radars(ind.get_coordinates(), 7)
plot_coverage(test_landscape)

radars = ind.count_radars()
```

```
uncovered = test_landscape.uncovered_count()

print(f'Radars: {radars}')
print(f'Uncovered Squares: {uncovered}')
```

Let's take a look at the following *figure 9.25* for a random 60x60 map:

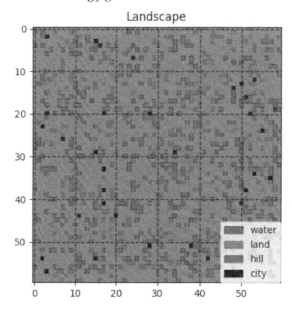

Figure 9.25: *Random 60×60 map*

Now, let's study the coverage figure without any radars. Red squares are cities that have to be covered by radar, as shown in the following *figure 9.26:*

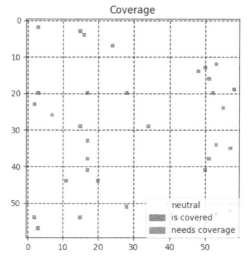

Figure 9.26: *Coverage map*

As we know, all squares have its own cost for radar placement (refer to the following *figure 9.27*):

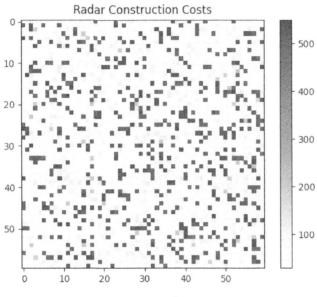

Figure 9.27: *Cost map*

Applying a random solution to the radar placement problem (refer to the following *figure 9.28*):

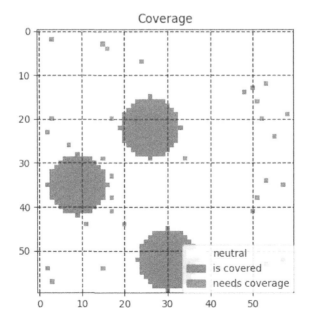

Figure 9.28: *Random Radars*

Obviously, the best solution assumes that all red squares will be covered with green.

We have determined the structure of the individual. Now you need to define the fitness function formula. Proceeding from the fact that we aim to minimize costs, then as a fitness function, we can take the cost of all the radars that the individual places. Also, the fitness function should terminate individuals that leave some cities uncovered; we used the same approach when designing the fitness function for the knapsack problem:

fitness function = - (uncovered cities × 500 + total radar costs)

So now, we are all ready to implement the GA that solves this problem, `ch9/radar/ga_general.py`:

Rank selection with elite, 3 point crossover and bit flip mutation

```python
def crossover(parent1, parent2):
    child1_genes, child2_genes = crossover_n_point(parent1.gene_list,
parent2.gene_list, 3)
    return Individual(child1_genes), Individual(child2_genes)

def mutate(ind):
    mut = mutation_bit_flip(ind.gene_list)
    return Individual(mut)

def select(population):
    return selection_rank_with_elite(population, elite_size = 2)
```

60×60 map size and radar radius equal to 7

```python
rows = 60
cols = 60
radar_radius = 7
```

Fitness function

```python
def fitness_function(coords):
    global landscape, radar_radius
    test_landscape = copy.deepcopy(landscape)
    test_landscape.add_radars(coords, radar_radius)
    return - test_landscape.uncovered_count() * 500 - test_landscape.
radar_cost()
```

GA parameters

```
POPULATION_SIZE = 60

CROSSOVER_PROBABILITY = .5

MUTATION_PROBABILITY = .5

MAX_GENERATIONS = 400
```

GA implementation

```
first_population = [Individual.generate_random(.005) for _ in
range(POPULATION_SIZE)]

best_ind = random.choice(first_population)

fit_avg = []

fit_best = []

generation_num = 0

population = first_population.copy()

generation_number = 0


while generation_num < MAX_GENERATIONS:

    generation_num += 1

    offspring = selection_rank_with_elite(population, elite_size = 2)

    crossed_offspring = crossover_operation(offspring, crossover,
CROSSOVER_PROBABILITY)

    mutated_offspring = mutation_operation(crossed_offspring, mutate,
MUTATION_PROBABILITY)

    population = mutated_offspring.copy()

    best_ind, fit_avg, fit_best = stats(population, best_ind, fit_avg, fit_
best)

    print(f'Generation {generation_num}. Avg fit: {fit_avg[-1]}. Best fit:
{best_ind.fitness}')


    test_landscape = copy.deepcopy(landscape)

    test_landscape.add_radars(best_ind.get_coordinates(), radar_radius)

    plot_coverage(test_landscape, title = f"Best Individual for
Generation: {generation_num}")


plot_stats(fit_avg, fit_best, "Radar Placement Problem")


plot_coverage(landscape, title = "Cities")

landscape.add_radars(best_ind.get_coordinates(), radar_radius)

plot_coverage(landscape, title = "Best Radar Placement")
```

```
print(f'Radar Count: {best_ind.count_radars()}')
print(f'Best Fitness: {best_ind.fitness}')
```

Result

Radar Count: 15

Best Fitness: -628

The best individual looks like as shown in following *figure 9.29:*

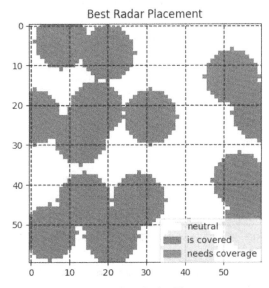

Figure 9.29: Best Radar Placement

And the statistics of the GA flow is shown in the following *figure 9.30:*

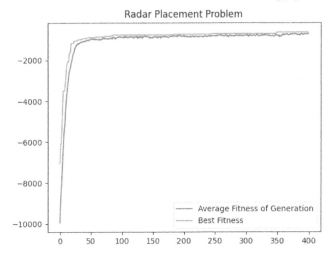

Figure 9.30: Genetic Algorithm Flow Statistics

Let's examine the behavior of the best individual through generations. Take a look at the following *figure 9.31:*

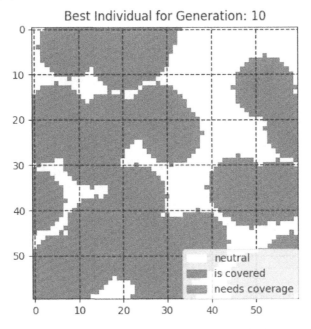

Figure 9.31: *Generation 10 – Best Individual*

Ten generations later (refer to the following *figure 9.32*):

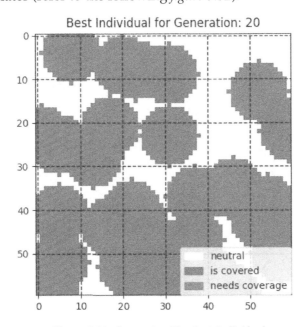

Figure 9.32: *Generation 20 – Best Individual*

And 30 generations later (refer to the following *figure 9.33*):

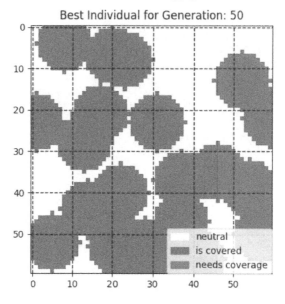

Figure 9.33: *Generation 50 – Best Individual*

But what's going on here? The best individual simply removes unnecessary radars but does not change their location in any way.

Take a look at the following *figure 9.34* for the best individual at the hundredth generation:

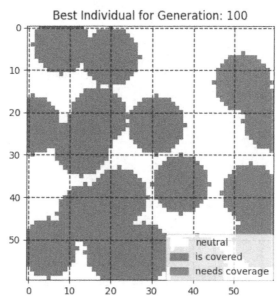

Figure 9.34: *Generation 100 – Best Individual*

This is a very inflexible evolutionary behavior. Now let's see how we could improve our algorithm. Let's take a closer look at how our mutation method works. Bit flip mutation means flipping a random gene, which means we remove or add a radar at a random location.

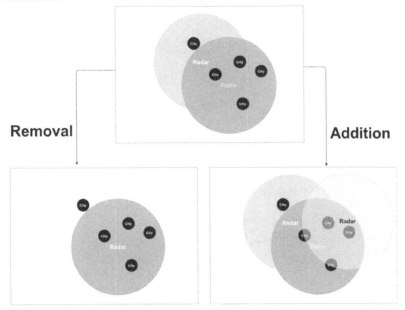

Figure 9.35: Radar Placement Bit Flip Mutation

Let's take a look at the preceding *figure 9.35*. Within the rules of our mutation, two options are possible. We remove any radar, but then immediately, one city comes out from under the coverage, thereby significantly reducing the mutated individual's fitness function, and excluding it from the population. The second option adds radar, but it only increases the radars' overall cost, and adds no benefit as it does not cover any new cities. But if you look closely at the diagram, the following solution may suggest itself (refer to the following *figure 9.36*):

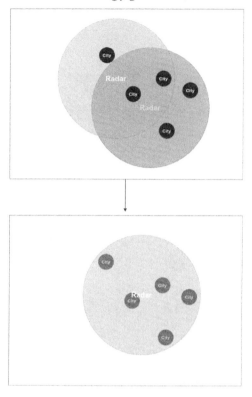

Figure 9.36: Radar Placement Shift Mutation

We remove one radar and shift toward the other. Of course, this is a positive mutation that improves the individual. We can naturally assume that such a mutation is a better evolutionary mechanism, and it is more logical to use it instead of the previous method of mutation.

Let's look at the solution that the algorithm will find, with an improved mutation method that allows you to remove radars and shift them, ch9/radar/toolbox.py:

Radar coordinate shift

```python
def mutation_shift_one(ind):
    mut = copy.deepcopy(ind.gene_list)
    one_poses = []

    for i in range(len(mut)):
        if mut[i] == 1:
            one_poses.append(i)
```

```
    one_pos = random.choice(one_poses)

    x_coord = one_pos % ind.rows
    y_coord = floor(one_pos / ind.rows)

    x_shifted = max(min(x_coord + random.randint(-10, 10), ind.cols -
1), 0)
    y_shifted = max(min(y_coord + random.randint(-10, 10), ind.rows -
1), 0)

    mut[y_shifted * ind.rows + x_shifted] = 1
    mut[one_pos] = 0

    return mut
```

Radar removal

```
def mutation_bit_flip_ones(ind):
    mut = copy.deepcopy(ind)
    one_pos = random.randint(0, sum(ind) - 1)

    i_one_pos = 0
    for i in range(len(ind)):
        if mut[i] == 1:
            if i_one_pos == one_pos:
                g1 = mut[i_one_pos]
                mut[i_one_pos] = (g1 + 1) % 2
                break
            else:
                i_one_pos += 1

    return mut
```

And we'll use the following mutation in our modified GA, ch9/radar/ga_modified.py:

```
def mutate(ind):
    if random.random() < .5:
        mut = mutation_bit_flip_ones(ind.gene_list)
    else:
        mut = mutation_shift_one(ind)
    return Individual(mut)
```

Result

Radar count: 14

Best Fitness: -431

The best individual in modified GA finds a much better solution – 14 radars with total cost 431, compared with – 15 radars with total cost 628 in previous solution.

The modified GA finds a solution much faster than the previous version. Take a look at the following *figure 9.37*:

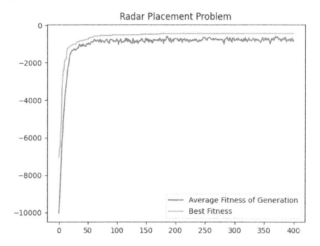

Figure 9.37: Modified Genetic Algorithm Flow Statistics

You can compare how the two solutions visually differ, as shown in the following *figure 9.38*:

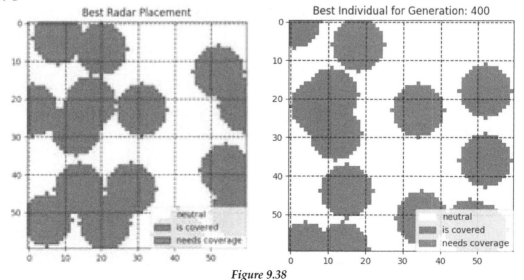

Figure 9.38

Left: The best individual of previous genetic algorithm implementation.

Right: The best individual of modified genetic algorithm.

> **NOTE : Do not forget that we have a condition of different costs for installing the radar on each square, which significantly complicates this problem.**

This example shows that there are no optimal selection, crossover, and mutation rules suitable for all cases in the implementation of GAs. Understanding exactly how a population evaluates, helps in parameters and methods tuning, which allows you to find solutions better and faster.

Conclusion

We showed the general principle of construction and automation, and searched for the optimal mechanism for knapsack problem. We learned that schedule problem represents another interesting class of problems. These problems have many solutions, and all correct solutions are equally good. If one solution can have a better fitness function value than another in the knapsack problem, then for tasks of the schedule problem class, all solutions have the same fitness function equal to 0. Radar problem is closer to real-time artificial intelligence systems, when the system needs to solve a geometric problem in short-time.

We saw how GAs can solve complex combinatorial problems without any idea about the nature and characteristics of the problem. After building the GA's architecture, we get a mechanism for solving not just a specific problem, but in general all problems of this class. Thus, you can automate the solution of many tasks without diving deeply into the complexity and subtleties of the issue.

This simplicity is the beauty and power of GAs. In the next chapter, we will look at how GAs solve other combinatorial problems.

Questions

1. Is it acceptable to use the shuffle mutation method in the radar placement problem?

2. Consider a modified knapsack problem. Let's say our backpack holds not 10kg, but 20kg. But at the airport, we are obliged to pay an extra 100$ for each kilogram of overweight. How do we change our fitness function need to be changed to address this challenge effectively?

3. Let's take a look at a common problem in machine learning. Suppose we have a set of some elements, and we need to divide them into two clusters. Which problem from the ones we considered earlier is closest to the clustering task?

    a) Knapsack problem

    b) Schedule problem

    c) Radar placement problem

CHAPTER 10
Combinatorial Optimization – Ordered Gene Encoding

In the previous chapter, we studied the combinatorial problems that can be solved using binary-encoded individuals. In this chapter, we will study the combinatorial problems, which are solved using ordered-encoded individuals.

Structure

In this chapter, we will cover the following topics:

- Travelling Salesman Problem
- Football Manager Problem

Objectives

- Explain how to adapt ordered encoded individuals for some class of combinatorial problems
- Understand how genetic algorithm solves them
- Define an architecture of genetic algorithm for combinatorial problems with ordered encoding

10.1 Travelling Salesman Problem

Travelling salesman problem is one of the most famous combinatorial optimization problems. It consists of finding the shortest route passing through the specified cities at least once, and then returning to the initial city. Let's take a look at the following *figure 10.1:*

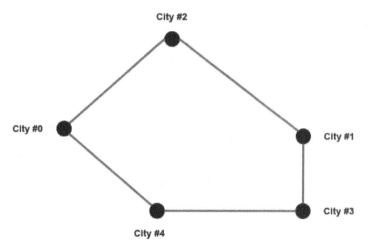

Figure 10.1: Travelling Salesman Problem

This may seem like a trivial intuitive task, but in general, this task is very complicated, and has no analytical solution. Let's see the coordinates of all US state capitals, in the following *figure 10.2:*

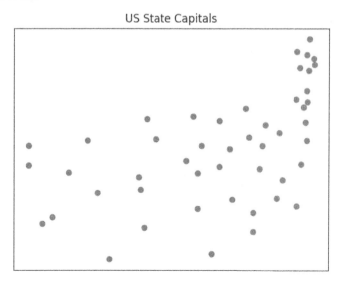

Figure 10.2: US State Capitals coordinates

It doesn't look so easy now, does it? But it's even more interesting to find out how many possible combinations of routes exist. Ready? Here is the number:

12931162075558409032148217757680598998459881619456 0000000000

Yes, that number equals to 48! / (48 × 2) or the number of all possible solutions of the problem of constructing the shortest tour of all 48 capitals of the US states. Of course, we cannot use a brute force search to solve such problems. But there is no analytical solution either. For this class of problems, the usage of GAs suits very well.

> **NOTE: The traveling salesman problem is very common in real life. For example, construction of air routes., or planning the shortest path in the car navigator.**

As you remember, ordered genes are genes that determine the order of certain numbers or values. Following we have an example of three ordered genes, as shown in *figure 10.3:*

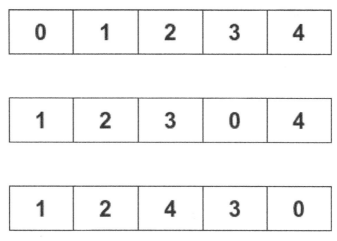

Figure 10.3: *Example of ordered genes*

In the context of the traveling salesman problem, an individual with ordered gene encoding defines a path. Let's consider an example of the problem of finding the shortest path between five cities. The shortest path will be determined by an individual with genes, as shown in the following *figure 10.4*:

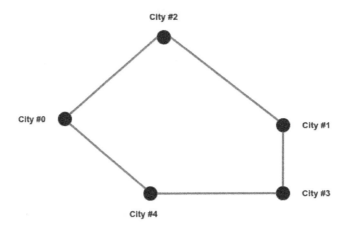

Figure 10.4: *Route represented by: (0, 2, 1, 3, 4)*

We see that within conditions of our task, it does not matter in which direction our salesman moves. So, the solutions: *(0, 2, 1, 3, 4)* and *(0, 4, 3, 1, 2)* are identical. And, also it does not matter from which city the salesman starts moving, hence the solutions, *(0, 2, 1, 3, 4), (2, 1, 3, 4, 0), (1, 3, 4, 0, 2), (3, 4, 0, 2, 1), (4, 0, 2, 1, 3)* are identical too. This means that the traveling salesman problem for n points has at least *(n × 2)* individuals that determine the same best solution.

Implementation of route length

The fitness function of a GA that will search for the shortest path is the distance of that path, ch10/tsp/route.py:

```
def distance(points, route):
    route_ext = copy.deepcopy(route)
    route_ext.append(route_ext[0])
    dist = 0
    for i in range(1, len(route_ext)):
        x_p = points[route_ext[i - 1]][0]
        x_c = points[route_ext[i]][0]
```

```
        y_p = points[route_ext[i - 1]][1]
        y_c = points[route_ext[i]][1]
        dist += pow((x_c - x_p)**2 + (y_c - y_p)**2, .5)
    return round(dist, 2)
```

Implementation of individual

Then we can define our individual as follows, ch10/tsp/individual.py:

```
import random
from ch10.tsp.route import distance, get_us_capitals, plot_route

class Individual:
    points = []

    def __init__(self, gene_list) -> None:
        self.gene_list = gene_list
        self.fitness = self.fitness_function()

    def fitness_function(self):
        return -distance(self.points, self.gene_list)
```

Creating a random individual is simply creating a random sequence of numbers *[0, 1, 2, ..., n-1]* :

```
def generate_random(points_num):
    route = list(range(points_num))
    random.shuffle(route)
    return Individual(route)
```

Let's study an example of applying a random individual to our problem:

```
if __name__ == '__main__':
    points = get_us_capitals()
    Individual.points = points
    ind = generate_random(len(points))
    plot_route(points, ind.gene_list)
```

Now, let's take a look at the following *figure 10.5*:

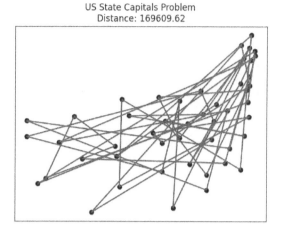

Figure 10.5: *Random Solution of US State Capitals Problem*

GA implementation

Yes, we can obviously assume that almost any random solution is very far from optimal. Well, let's move on to building a genetic algorithm, `ch10/tsp/ga.py`.

We will use fitness driven ordered crossover, fitness driven shift mutation, and rank selection with elite:

```
def crossover(parent1, parent2):
    return crossover_fitness_driven_order(parent1, parent2)
```

```
def mutate(ind):
    return mutation_fitness_driven_shift(ind)
```

```
def select(population):
    return selection_rank_with_elite(population, elite_size = 2)
```

We set the points on the map:

```
points = get_us_capitals()
Individual.points = points
```

Parameters of genetic algorithm:

```
POPULATION_SIZE = 200
CROSSOVER_PROBABILITY = .3
MUTATION_PROBABILITY = .9
MAX_GENERATIONS = 300
```

And structure of genetic algorithm:

```
first_population = [generate_random(len(points)) for _ in
range(POPULATION_SIZE)]
best_ind = random.choice(first_population)
fit_avg = []
fit_best = []
generation_num = 0
population = first_population.copy()
generation_number = 0

while generation_num < MAX_GENERATIONS:
    generation_num += 1
    offspring = selection_rank_with_elite(population, elite_size = 2)
    crossed_offspring = crossover_operation(offspring, crossover,
CROSSOVER_PROBABILITY)
    mutated_offspring = mutation_operation(crossed_offspring, mutate,
MUTATION_PROBABILITY)
    population = mutated_offspring.copy()
    best_ind, fit_avg, fit_best = stats(population, best_ind, fit_avg, fit_
best)
    print(f'{generation_num} from {MAX_GENERATIONS}: {fit_avg[-1]}'

plot_stats(fit_avg, fit_best, "US State Capital Tour Problem")
plot_route(points, best_ind.gene_list)
```

Result

The solution which GA finds looks like the following *figure 10.6:*

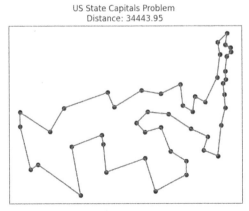

US State Capitals Problem
Distance: 34443.95

Figure 10.6: *Solution of US State Capitals Problem*

This solution looks very nice. However, this is not the best solution. Resource **https:// people.sc.fsu.edu/~jburkardt/datasets/tsp/tsp.html** declares that the best solution has a length equal to 33523. Yes, we know that the GA does not always find the best solution of all possible ones, but the solution we found with a length of **34443.95** is not very far from the best solution **33523**.

The progress of evolution looks like the following *figure 10.7:*

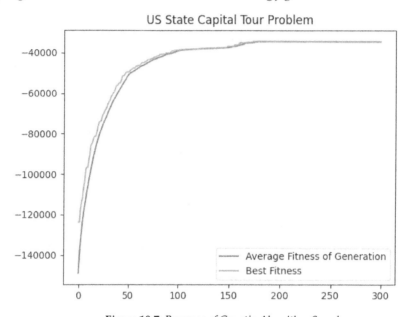

Figure 10.7: *Progress of Genetic Algorithm Search*

Everything looks good. We analyzed the problem, created the individual's structure, and determined the fitness function, and architecture of the genetic algorithm. All our actions look quite reasonable, except for the design of the genetic algorithm. Why did we decide that this particular design would be better suited for this task?

Take a look at the following *figure 10.8:*

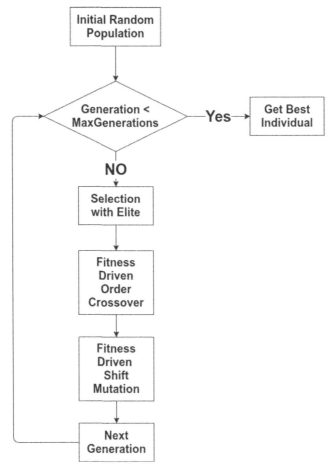

Figure 10.8: Design of Genetic Algorithm for Travelling Salesman Problem

Comparison between shift mutation and shuffle mutation

Let's do some research on how the genetic algorithm's efficiency will change if we change the mutation operation from shift mutation to shuffle mutation.

To do this, we will run a Monte Carlo simulation on both of these algorithms, and compare the results, ch9/knapsack/ga_shift_vs_shuffle_mutation.py.

We define two mutation methods:

```
def mutate_shift(ind):
    return mutation_fitness_driven_shift(ind)
```

```
def mutate_shuffle(ind):
    return mutation_fitness_driven_shuffle(ind)
```

We set parameters for test run, and run each algorithm 100 times:

```
RUNS = 100
TEST_PARAMETERS = {
    'Shuffle Mutation': mutation_fitness_driven_shuffle,
    'Shift Mutation':   mutation_fitness_driven_shift
}
CROSSOVER_PROBABILITY = .3
MUTATION_PROBABILITY = .9
POPULATION_SIZE = 200
MAX_GENERATIONS = 200
```

And the Monte-Carlo simulation:

```
results = [None] * len(TEST_PARAMETERS)
counter = [None] * len(TEST_PARAMETERS)

for design in range(len(TEST_PARAMETERS)):

    results[design] = []
    counter[design] = []

    mutate = list(TEST_PARAMETERS.values())[design]

    print(f'Testing : {list(TEST_PARAMETERS.keys())[design]}')

    for r in range(RUNS):
        Individual.count = 0
        first_population = [generate_random(len(points)) for _ in
range(POPULATION_SIZE)]
        best_ind = random.choice(first_population)
        fit_avg = []
        fit_best = []
        generation_num = 0
        population = first_population.copy()
        generation_number = 0

        while generation_num < MAX_GENERATIONS:
            generation_num += 1
            offspring = selection_rank_with_elite(population, elite_size
= 2)
```

```
        crossed_offspring = crossover_operation(offspring,
crossover, CROSSOVER_PROBABILITY)
        mutated_offspring = mutation_operation(crossed_offspring,
mutate, MUTATION_PROBABILITY)
        population = mutated_offspring.copy()
        best_ind, fit_avg, fit_best = stats(population, best_ind, fit_
avg, fit_best)

    results[design].append(fit_best[-1])
    counter[design].append(Individual.count)

    print(f'Best Individual: {fit_best[-1]} for run: {r}')
```

For convenience, we visualize the results:

```
plt.boxplot([results[0], results[1]])
plt.title("Best Individual Distribution \n Shuffle Mutation VS Shift
Mutation")
plt.xticks(range(1, len(TEST_PARAMETERS) + 1), TEST_PARAMETERS.keys())
plt.show()

plt.boxplot([counter[0], counter[1]])
plt.title("Total Number of Individuals Distribution \n Shuffle Mutation
VS Shift Mutation")
plt.xticks(range(1, len(TEST_PARAMETERS) + 1), TEST_PARAMETERS.keys())
plt.show()
```

Result

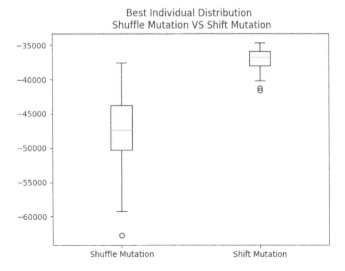

Figure 10.9: Comparison of the Results of the Two Algorithms

As shown in the preceding *figure 10.9*, obviously, an algorithm using shift mutation as the mutation operation shows much better results. The algorithm using shift mutation is very likely to provide a result in the range from 35,000 to 40,000, while the average value of the fitness function of the algorithm using shuffle mutation is about 48,000.

We also need to compare the distribution of the total number of individuals participating in the evolution.

Let's take a look at the following *figure 10.10:*

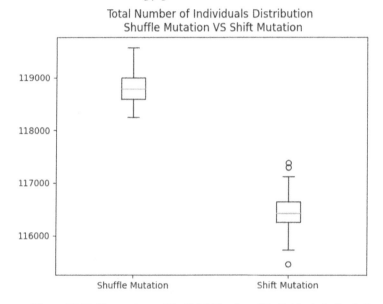

Figure 10.10: Comparison of the Total Number of Individuals in Evolution

As you can see, the individuals' total value in both algorithms is very close, but the algorithm using shift mutation usually uses fewer individuals during the entire evolution. Thus, we come to a clear understanding that the algorithm using shift mutation is significantly superior to the algorithm using shuffle mutation.

By experimenting with the genetic algorithm's various parameters and methods, you can choose the most suitable architecture for a certain class of problems.

10.2 Football manager problem

This section will study a problem familiar to all football fans and gamers playing any football manager simulator. What if we were the head of a football club and our task would be to build a football team from scratch with a predefined budget. Yes, everyone who has ever been fond of team sports has wondered what kind of players he would invite to his team. This is a problem that inspires so many amateurs and professionals. Let's try to formulate this task into a mathematical form to build the strongest team that can be built within the available budget. We have downloaded a list of all football players from the FIFA 2020 football simulator database. The list is available here: https://www.kaggle.com/stefanoleone992/fifa-20-complete-player-dataset. In this database, we are only concerned with the following values – player name, position in the club, skills, age and price – as shown in the following table:

Name	Position	Skills	Age	Price
L. Messi	RW	94	32	95.500.000 €
C. Ronaldo	LW	93	34	58.500.000 €
Neymar Jr	CAM	92	27	105.500.000 €
J. Oblak	GK	91	26	77.500.000 €
E. Hazard	LW	91	28	90.000.000 €
...				

So, our task can be formulated as follows – having a budget of 500 million euros to buy such players, so that the average score of the team's skills will be maximum. Simultaneously, this task has natural limitations. We cannot consider a good team which consists only of goalkeepers, defenders or forwards. The team must consist of 23 players, at least two goalkeepers, five defenders, five midfielders, and four forwards. On top of that, we want to create a young and promising team, so we'd rather give preference to a young player, even if his skills are slightly lower to a mature player.

Let's try to determine how an individual, which represents some solution to this problem, should look like. Obviously, the task comes down to the fact that we need to list 23 players from the entire player database, that is, the task is reduced to return a list of 23 numbers, where each number is the serial number of the player.

The individual in this problem has ordered gene encoding, where the first 23 genes determine the command (refer to the following *figure 10.11*):

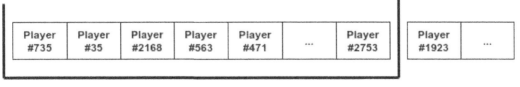

23 Players

Figure 10.11: Individual Representation for Football Manager Problem

Implementation of individual

The individual can be defined in the following way, `ch10/football_manager/individual.py`:

```python
class Individual:
    team_size = 23

    @classmethod
    def set_fitness_function(cls, fun):
        cls.fitness_function = fun

    def __init__(self, gene_list) -> None:
        self.gene_list = gene_list
        self.fitness = self.__class__.fitness_function(self.get_team())

    def get_team(self):
        return self.gene_list[:self.__class__.team_size]
```

And random individual generator:

```python
def generate_random(base_size):
    players_idx = list(range(base_size))
    random.shuffle(players_idx)
    return Individual(players_idx)
```

Position restrictions

For the correct team selection, it is necessary to determine the limit on the team's number of players' positions, `ch10/football_manager/football.py`:

```python
def position_violations(players_df, team, min_positions, max_positions):
    team_df = players_df[players_df.index.isin(team)]
    team_positions = {}
    for _, row in team_df.iterrows():
        pos = row['position']
        if pos in team_positions.keys():
            team_positions[pos] += 1
        else:
            team_positions[pos] = 1

    violations = 0

    for k in list(min_positions.keys()):
```

```
        if k not in team_positions.keys() or min_positions[k] > team_
positions[k]:
            violations += 1

    for k in list(max_positions.keys()):
        if k not in team_positions.keys() or max_positions[k] < team_
positions[k]:
            violations += 1

    return violations
```

Team info

Other functions are helper methods that return team information:

```
def team_price(players_df, team):
    team_df = players_df[players_df.index.isin(team)]
    return team_df['price'].sum()

def team_skill(players_df, team):
    team_df = players_df[players_df.index.isin(team)]
    return round(team_df['skills'].sum() / len(team), 2)

def team_age(players_df, team):
    team_df = players_df[players_df.index.isin(team)]
    return round(team_df['age'].sum() / len(team), 2)

def team_print(players_df, team):
    position_map = {
        'G': 'Goalkeepers',
        'D': 'Defenders',
        'M': 'Midfielders',
        'F': 'Forwards'
    }

    for k, v in position_map.items():
        print(f'\n{v}:')
        team_df = players_df[players_df.index.isin(team)]
        for _, row in team_df[team_df['position'] == k].sort_values(by =
'skills').iterrows():
            print(f"{row['name']} ({row['club']}). "
                f"Skill: {row['skills']}. Price: {'{:,}'.
```

```
format(row['price'])}. Age: {row['age']}")
```

Implementation of fitness function

The next step is to define what our fitness function will look like.

- First , we need to maximize the average of the team's skills.
- Second, do not go beyond the established budget.
- Third, a certain set of positions must be represented in the team.
- Lastly, we must prioritize the selection of younger players. A possible variant of such a fitness function is the following method:

```
def fitness_function(team):
    team_str = ','.join([str(i) for i in team])
    min_positions = {'G': 2, 'D': 5, 'M': 5, 'F': 4}
    max_positions = {'G': 3, 'D': 7, 'M': 9, 'F': 6}
    skills = team_skill(player_base_df, team)
    if team_price(player_base_df, team) > 500_000_000:
        return 0
    age = team_age(player_base_df, team)
    violations = position_violations(player_base_df, team, min_
positions, max_positions)
    val = skills * (1 - violations * .1) * (100 - age / 2) / 100
    return val
```

Implementation of genetic algorithm

So, we are ready to start recruiting our dream team, `ch10/football_manager/ga.py`.

As in the preceding example, we will use the same genetic algorithm architecture, fitness driven ordered crossover, fitness driven shift mutation, and rank selection with elite:

```
def crossover(parent1, parent2):
    return crossover_fitness_driven_order(parent1, parent2)


def mutate(ind):
    return mutation_fitness_driven_shift(ind)


def select(population):
    return selection_rank_with_elite(population, elite_size = 2)
```

Parameters of genetic algoritm:

```
POPULATION_SIZE = 400
CROSSOVER_PROBABILITY = .3
MUTATION_PROBABILITY = .8
MAX_GENERATIONS = 400
```

And the genetic algorithm:

```
first_population = [generate_random(len(player_base_df)) for _ in
range(POPULATION_SIZE)]
best_ind = random.choice(first_population)
fit_avg = []
fit_best = []
generation_num = 0
population = first_population.copy()
generation_number = 0

while generation_num < MAX_GENERATIONS:
    generation_num += 1
    offspring = selection_rank_with_elite(population, elite_size = 2)
    crossed_offspring = crossover_operation(offspring, crossover,
CROSSOVER_PROBABILITY)
    mutated_offspring = mutation_operation(crossed_offspring, mutate,
MUTATION_PROBABILITY)
    population = mutated_offspring.copy()
    best_ind, fit_avg, fit_best = stats(population, best_ind, fit_avg, fit_
best)
    print(
        f'Generation {generation_num} from {MAX_GENERATIONS}. '
        f'Avg fit: {round(fit_avg[-1], 2)}. '
        f'Best fit: {round(best_ind.fitness,2)}. '
        f'Skills: {team_skill(player_base_df, best_ind.get_team())} '
        f'Price: {team_price(player_base_df, best_ind.get_team())} '
        f'Age: {team_age(player_base_df, best_ind.get_team())}')

    if generation_num % 25 == 0:
        team_print(player_base_df, best_ind.get_team())


plot_stats(fit_avg, fit_best, "Football Manager Problem")
```

Result

And as a result, we get the following team:

Goalkeepers:

P. Bernardoni (Nîmes Olympique). Skill: 77. Price: 9,500,000. Age: 22

W. Benítez (OGC Nice). Skill: 80. Price: 13,500,000. Age: 26

T. Strakosha (Lazio). Skill: 82. Price: 22,000,000. Age: 24

Defenders:

F. Bustos (Independiente). Skill: 77. Price: 11,000,000. Age: 23

Rúben Dias (SL Benfica). Skill: 80. Price: 18,500,000. Age: 22

Sidnei (Real Betis). Skill: 80. Price: 12,500,000. Age: 29

André Almeida (SL Benfica). Skill: 81. Price: 15,000,000. Age: 28

L. Digne (Everton). Skill: 83. Price: 28,500,000. Age: 25

Pepe (FC Porto). Skill: 84. Price: 6,500,000. Age: 36

Marquinhos (Paris Saint-Germain). Skill: 86. Price: 51,500,000. Age: 25

Midfielders:

S. McTominay (Manchester United). Skill: 77. Price: 11,500,000. Age: 22

Bruma (PSV). Skill: 78. Price: 13,000,000. Age: 24

Vinícius Jr. (Real Madrid). Skill: 79. Price: 22,500,000. Age: 18

Raphinha (Sporting CP). Skill: 79. Price: 17,000,000. Age: 22

M. Sanson (Olympique de Marseille). Skill: 79. Price: 16,000,000. Age: 24

D. Klaassen (SV Werder Bremen). Skill: 80. Price: 17,000,000. Age: 26

Rúben Neves (Wolverhampton Wanderers). Skill: 82. Price: 29,000,000. Age: 22

K. Coman (FC Bayern München). Skill: 84. Price: 40,500,000. Age: 23

Sergio Busquets (FC Barcelona). Skill: 89. Price: 55,000,000. Age: 30

Forwards:

Alex Berenguer (Torino). Skill: 77. Price: 12,000,000. Age: 23

M. Gaćinović (Eintracht Frankfurt). Skill: 77. Price: 12,000,000. Age: 24

M. Arnautović (Shanghai SIPG FC). Skill: 82. Price: 21,500,000. Age: 30

D. Alli (Tottenham Hotspur). Skill: 84. Price: 41,500,000. Age: 23

Our team has the following characteristics:

Price: 497,000,000 €

Average Skills: 80.74

Average Age: 24.83

We've selected a young and skilled team. Let's show the genetic algorithm progress (refer to the following *figure 10.12*):

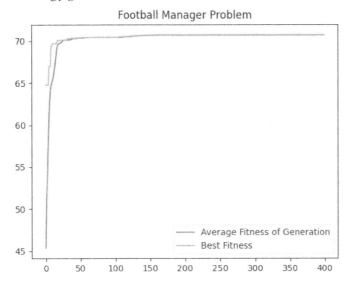

Figure 10.12: *Progress of Genetic Algorithm Search*

The football manager problem is a good example of the widespread use of genetic algorithms.

Conclusion

In this chapter, we studied how genetic algorithms with ordered gene encoding can be applied to completely different classes of problems, none of which have an analytical solution. As you can see, the most challenging part of the task is to correctly determine an individual's structure and fitness function.

In the next chapter, we will look at some more interesting practical problems that can also be solved using genetic algorithms.

Questions

1. When we compared the effectiveness of two different mutation methods for the traveling salesman problem in Section 10.1, we found that, on average, fitness driven shuffle mutation evolution produces more individuals than fitness driven shift mutation evolution (*figure 10.10*). Although the parameters of GAs (population size, crossover probability, mutation probability) are the same. How can this be explained?

2. In problems with ordered gene encoding, we used an unusual combination of GA parameters, a high probability of mutation, and a low probability of crossover. Try to test, and compare how the algorithm's performance will change if you use a high probability of crossover and a low probability of mutation.

## CHAPTER 11

Other Common Problems

In the previous two chapters, we observed different types of combinatorial problems, and we already have a deep understanding of the issues, and how the genetic algorithms are applied. In this chapter, we will look at some more example tasks. The purpose of this chapter is to broaden the horizon of problems solved using genetic algorithms.

Structure

In this chapter, we will cover the following topics:

- System of equations
- Graph coloring problem

Objective

To get familiar with other types of problems.

11.1 System of equations

In real life, problems often arise that lead to the appearance of a system of equations. Moreover, this equation system can be very complicated, and sometimes, it cannot even be analytically solvable. Methods of finding solutions based on genetic algorithms are very well suited for such problems.

Let us have a system of equations:

$$\begin{cases} f(x, y, z) = 0 \\ g(x, y, z) = 0 \\ w(x, y, z) = 0 \end{cases}$$

As we remember, (x, y, z) satisfies the system of equations, if and only if (x, y, z) satisfies the equation:

$$|f(x,y,z)| + |g(x,y,z)| + |w(x,y,z)| = 0$$

Therefore, all we need to do is find the points at which the function:

$f(x, y, z) = |f(x,y,z)| + |g(x,y,z)| + |w(x,y,z)| = 0$, or find the minimum of this function.

Let's try to solve the following system of equations in integers:

$$\begin{cases} (xy + 2)x^2 + (x+y)^{|z-2|^8+2} + xyz = 0 \\ x(yz + 10) - |z - 3|! + y^{|x|} + 11z = 0 \\ (x + 7y)^{|z+x|} - (z + 16)^2 - 151 = 0 \end{cases}$$

Implementation of genetic algorithm

The genetic algorithm will have an already familiar structure to us, ch11/system_of_equations/ga.py.

System of equations

```
def f(x, y, z):
    return (x * y + 2)**2 + (x + y)**(abs(z - 2)**3 + 2) + x * y * z

def g(x, y, z):
    return x * (y * z + 10) - factorial(abs(z - 3)) + y**abs(x) + 11 * z

def w(x, y, z):
    return (x + 7 * y)**abs(z + x) - (z + 16)**2 - 151
```

Fitness function

```
def F(x, y, z):
    return abs(f(x, y, z)) + abs(g(x, y, z)) + abs(w(x, y, z))
```

Individual

```
class Individual:
```

```python
    def __init__(self, gene_list) -> None:
        self.gene_list = [constraints(g) for g in gene_list]
        self.fitness = -F(self.gene_list[0], self.gene_list[1], self.
gene_list[2])

    def __str__(self):
        return f'x: {self.gene_list[0]}, y: {self.gene_list[1]}, z:
{self.gene_list[2]}, fitness: {self.fitness}'
```

Genetic algorithm structure

```python
def crossover(parent1, parent2):
    child1_genes, child2_genes = crossover_blend(parent1.gene_list,
parent2.gene_list, 0.8)
    return Individual(child1_genes), Individual(child2_genes)

def mutate(ind):
    mutated_gene = mutation_random_deviation(ind.gene_list, 0, 3, 0.5)
    return Individual(mutated_gene)

def select(population):
    return selection_rank_with_elite(population, elite_size = 2)

def create_random():
    return Individual([
        round(random.uniform(-10, 10), 2),
        round(random.uniform(-10, 10), 2),
        round(random.uniform(-10, 10), 2)
    ])
```

Genetic algorithm parameters

```python
POPULATION_SIZE = 400
CROSSOVER_PROBABILITY = .8
MUTATION_PROBABILITY = .4
MAX_GENERATIONS = 100
```

Genetic algorithm flow

And in genetic algorithm flow, we stop the evolution cycle, if best fitness equals to zero:

```python
first_population = [create_random() for _ in range(POPULATION_SIZE)]
best_ind = random.choice(first_population)
```

```
generation_number = 0

population = first_population.copy()

while generation_number < MAX_GENERATIONS and best_ind.fitness != 0:
    generation_number += 1
    offspring = select(population)
    crossed_offspring = crossover_operation(offspring, crossover,
CROSSOVER_PROBABILITY)
    mutated_offspring = mutation_operation(crossed_offspring, mutate,
MUTATION_PROBABILITY)
    population = mutated_offspring.copy()

    best_of_generation = max(population, key = lambda ind: ind.fitness)
    if best_ind.fitness < best_of_generation.fitness:
        best_ind = best_of_generation
    print(f'Generation: {generation_number}, best fit: {best_ind.
fitness}')

print(f'Best Individual : {best_ind}')
```

Result
Best Individual : x: -6, y: 2, z: 3, fitness: 0

This is a pretty straightforward approach that can give good results.

11.2 Graph coloring problem

As we remember, the graph is some structure with vertices and edges connecting them, as shown in the following *figure 11.1:*

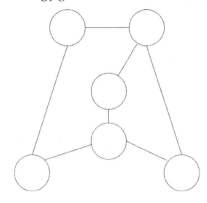

Figure 11.1: Graph Example

A large number of problems from game theory, chemistry, biology, and social networks analysis are formulated as graph theory problems. One of the important subclasses of graph theory problems is the graph coloring problem. The graph coloring problem is formulated as follows – for a given graph, it is necessary to color its vertices with some colors to satisfy the specified condition.

Let's solve the following graph coloring problem. It is necessary to color the graph vertices from *figure 11.1* using three colors, so that there will be no single pair of adjacent vertices with the same color. Take a look at the following *figure 11.2*:

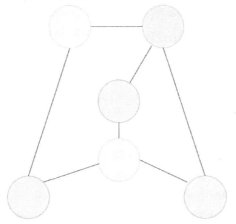

Figure 11.2: *Graph Coloring Problem Example*

Well, the solution used in the preceding figure doesn't seem that difficult, does it? It is relatively easy to solve this problem without using any additional tools. Then let's try to examine the graph with 30 vertices in the following *figure 11.3*:

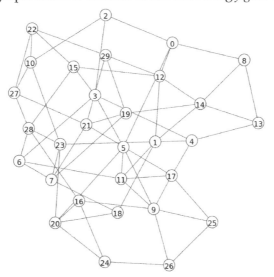

Figure 11.3: *30 Vertices Graph for Graph Coloring Problem*

As you can see, the example on the preceding figure is already more complicated. Let's try to solve the graph coloring problem using a genetic algorithm.

Graph functions

First, let's study how we will work with the graph, `ch11/graph/graph_utils.py`.

We will use the following additional libraries – `python-igraph`, `cairocffi`.

```
pip install python-igraph
pip install cairocffi
```

Colored graph plotting function

```
def plot_graph(edges, vertex_color):
    g = Graph(directed = False)
    g.add_vertices(len(get_vertices_from_edges(edges)))

    for i in range(len(g.vs)):
        g.vs[i]["id"] = i
        g.vs[i]["label"] = str(i)
        g.vs[i]['color'] = vertex_color[i]

    g.add_edges(edges)

    visual_style = {
        "bbox":               (800, 800),
        "margin":             27,
        "vertex_size":        35,
        "vertex_label_size":  22,
        "edge_curved":        False,
        "layout":             g.layout_lgl()
    }
    plot(g, **visual_style)
```

Fitness function

And a helper function that counts connected vertices of the same color, this function will be used as a fitness function:

```
def adjacent_vertices_same_color_count(edges, vertex_color):
    color_map = {}
    for vertex, color in vertex_color.items():
        if color not in color_map:
```

```
            color_map[color] = set()
        color_map[color].add(vertex)

    count = 0
    for edge in edges:
        for _, vertices in color_map.items():
            if set(edge) <= set(vertices):
                count += 1

    return count
```

Implementation of individual

An individual in this problem is represented by a list of genes of length corresponding to the number of vertices, where each gene determines the color of the vertex. In our case, an individual is a list of 30 elements from the set (0,1,2), where 0 is red, 1 is green, 2 is blue, ch11/graph/individual.py.

Definition of individual

```
class Individual:
    color_map = {
        0: "red",
        1: "green",
        2: "blue"
    }

    vertex_number = 0
    edges = []

    def __init__(self, gene_list) -> None:
        self.gene_list = gene_list
        self.fitness = - adjacent_vertices_same_color_count(self.__
class__.edges, self.vertex_colors())

    def vertex_colors(self):
        vertex_colors = {}
        for i in range(len(self.gene_list)):
            vertex_colors[i] = self.__class__.color_map[self.gene_
list[i]]
        return vertex_colors

    @classmethod
```

```
def generate_random(cls):
    gene_list = random.choices(list(cls.color_map.keys()), k = cls.
vertex_number)
    return Individual(gene_list)
```

Random individual

Now, let's try to generate a random individual for our problem:

```
if __name__ == '__main__':

    random.seed(1)

    edges = get_edges()
    Individual.vertex_number = len(get_vertices_from_edges(edges))
    Individual.edges = edges

    ind = Individual.generate_random()
    print(ind.fitness)
    plot_graph(Individual.edges, ind.vertex_colors())
```

Result

Fitness: -20

Take a look at the following *figure 11.4:*

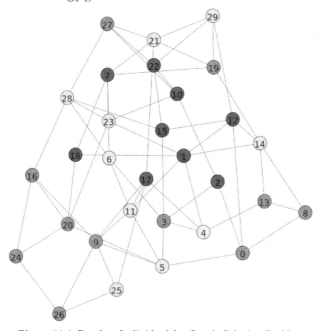

Figure 11.4: Random Individual for Graph Coloring Problem

Implementation of genetic algorithm

Let's build a genetic algorithm solving graph coloring problem, `ch11/graph/ga.py`.

We use rank selection with elite, 2-point fitness driven crossover, and fitness driven random change mutation. Random change mutation is a simple random choice of one of three colors. It means that a random gene in the gene list will be changed to a random color:

```python
def crossover(parent1, parent2):
    return crossover_fitness_driven_n_point(parent1, parent2, 2)

def mutate(ind):
    return mutation_fitness_driven_random_change(ind, range(3), 3)

def select(population):
    return selection_rank_with_elite(population, elite_size = 2)
```

Genetic algorithm parameters

```python
POPULATION_SIZE = 500
CROSSOVER_PROBABILITY = .5
MUTATION_PROBABILITY = .5
MAX_GENERATIONS = 200
```

Genetic algorithm flow

```python
first_population = [Individual.generate_random() for _ in
range(POPULATION_SIZE)]
best_ind = random.choice(first_population)
generation_number = 0

population = first_population.copy()

while generation_number < MAX_GENERATIONS and best_ind.fitness != 0:
    generation_number += 1
    offspring = select(population)
    crossed_offspring = crossover_operation(offspring, crossover,
CROSSOVER_PROBABILITY)
    mutated_offspring = mutation_operation(crossed_offspring, mutate,
MUTATION_PROBABILITY)
    population = mutated_offspring.copy()

    best_of_generation = max(population, key = lambda ind: ind.fitness)
    if best_ind.fitness < best_of_generation.fitness:
```

```
        best_ind = best_of_generation
    print(f'Generation: {generation_number}, best fit: {best_ind.
fitness}')

print(f'Best Individual Fitness: {best_ind.fitness}')
plot_graph(edges, best_ind.vertex_colors())
```

Result

Take a look at the following figure *11.5:*

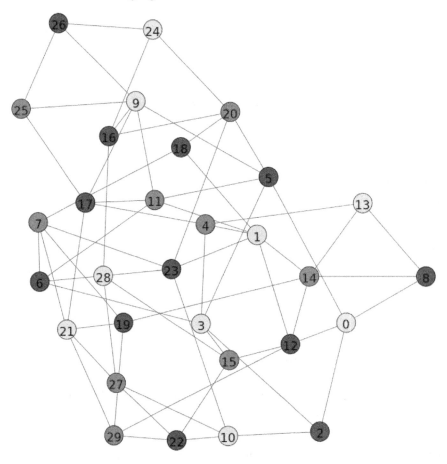

Figure 11.5: *Solution of Graph Coloring Problem*

Nice, we can see how the genetic algorithm has found one of the suitable solutions for coloring the graph, in which none of the adjacent vertices has the same color.

Conclusion

In this chapter, we have provided more examples of the use of genetic algorithms. We hope that the reader has an intuitive idea of the classes of problems in which genetic algorithms can be successfully applied.

We have finished studying the practical applications of genetic algorithms. Of course, these examples are far from covering the many variations of the genetic algorithm applications. In the next chapter, we'll look at various ways to modify and increase genetic algorithms' efficiency.

Questions

1. Say we have the following system of equations:

$$\begin{cases} f(x, y, z) = 0 \\ g(x, y, z) = 0| \\ w(x, y, z) = 0 \end{cases}$$

   And we have to find a solution to the problem in which the value of the function $l(x, y, z)$ will be maximum. Which fitness function should be used to solve this problem?

2. Is it possible to solve the graph color problem for the graph in *figure 11.2* using only two colors?

CHAPTER 12
Adaptive Genetic Algorithm

In the previous chapters, we have studied many practical problems that are solved using genetic algorithms. In each of these tasks, we had to determine the structure of an individual, fitness function, and architecture of the genetic algorithm. But in addition to this, a significant action was to determine the parameters of the genetic algorithm – population size, mutation probability and crossover probability . The efficiency of the genetic algorithm often depended on the correct choice of these parameters. But the right choice of these parameters is a complicated task, which we solved intuitively.

However, what if we do not want or do not have the ability to select the parameters that are best suited for a certain class of problems? What if the genetic algorithm in the process of evolution will itself adjust the parameters of the population, mutation, and crossover?

We can leave the genetic algorithm to decide which parameters to use for the current generation. This approach will eliminate the problem of correct selection of parameters and completely automate the search process. Genetic algorithms that change their behavior during evolution are called adaptive. In this chapter, we will explore the adaptive genetic algorithms.

Structure

In this chapter, we will cover the following topics:

- Evolutionary improvement rate
- Evolutionary progress and population size
- Evolutionary progress, crossover, and mutation probability
- Evolutionary dead end and premature termination of the genetic algorithm
- Example of adaptive genetic algorithm
- Adaptive genetic algorithm versus classical genetic algorithm

Objectives

The main objectives of this chapter are as follows:

- To explain what is evolutionary improvement and degradation
- To know what genetic algorithm can do to start improving after a degradation
- To give an example of adaptive genetic algorithm
- To compare adaptive genetic algorithm and classical genetic algorithm

12.1 Evolutionary improvement rate

To make our adaptive genetic algorithm to reconfigure its parameters somehow, we need to answer the following question – What is happening now with the evolutionary process, and how successful is it? The answer to this question is that the algorithm will be able to decide how to reconfigure its parameters. The question can be simplified as follows – Is our population improving or not? Does the average value of the population fitness function grow with increasing generations?

Implementation of population improvement

We define the improvement rate as the deviation of the current population's average fitness function from the average fitness function for n generations in the past. If the deviation of the current population's fitness function exceeds the average fitness function for n generations in the past by x percent, then we define that the population is developing. We define that a population degrades if it does not improve; so any population without improvement is degradation, `ch12/evolution_stats.py`:

```python
import math
from math import nan


def average(series, period):
    if len(series) < period:
```

```
        return nan
    else:
        return sum(series[-period - 1:-1]) / period

def is_improvement_positive(population_fit, period = 10, gap = .01):
    avg = average(population_fit, period)
    if math.isnan(avg) or avg == 0:
        return True
    return population_fit[-1] > avg * (1 - gap)
```

Let's look at the intervals of improvement, and degradation of the population using a specific example of the genetic algorithm for solving the traveling salesman problem, ch12/ga_improvement.py:

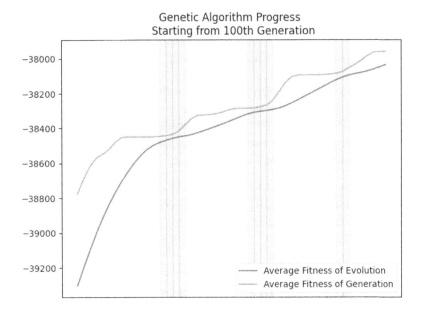

Figure 12.1: Population Improvement Intervals

In the preceding *figure 12.1*, we mark the population degradation intervals using red bars. We see that as soon as the average fitness function curve tends to be flat, we state that the population has stopped improving.

12.2 Evolutionary progress and population size

As we already know, in the genetic algorithm each individual represents some kind of an explorer who offers his solution to the problem. The more explorers we have, the higher the likelihood of successful population improvement.

If evolution is improving well, and the fitness function of each population is higher than the previous one, then we do not need many individuals. This means that individuals have already found some evolutionary path, and are moving along that.

The opposite situation arises if the population begins to degrade. This means that the population is facing an evolutionary dead end, and more scouts are needed to look for an evolutionary way out of this dead end.

Thus, we can formulate the following rule:

- We decrease the population size, if the population improves.
- We increase the population size, if the population degrades.

This approach to population size management can seem very counterintuitive. Indeed, in nature, a successful species, on the contrary, due to its fitness, increases its numbers, and vice versa. When a species cannot adapt to the environment, then its population begins to decline until it completely disappears. Yes, this behavior takes place in the wild because, in the wild, each individual's goal is to spread their genes. In a genetic algorithm, an individual's goal is to find the best solution. We can increase and decrease populations with one line of code if we want.

Why are we concerned about population size at all? Why not keep it constant? The size of the population dramatically affects the computational resources consumed by the genetic algorithm. Therefore, it makes sense to rebalance them so that more resources of the algorithm are used in those places where the population is experiencing evolutionary degradation.

12.3 Evolutionary progress, crossover, and mutation probabilities

The result of crossover is the generation of new individuals with mixed parental genes. The appearance of such individuals always increases the likelihood of finding the best solution. Still, at the same time, the generation of new individuals is a resource-consuming operation for the genetic algorithm.

If our population improves well, and the probability that at least one child will be better than their parents, then we can limit the number of crossovers in the population. Conversely, suppose a population suffers from evolutionary degradation; in that case, it is necessary to increase the number of crossovers in order to find an individual that will discover a new useful combination of genes.

Thus, we can formulate the following rule:

- We decrease the crossover probability, if the population improves.
- We increase the crossover probability, if the population degrades.

The situation is similar in mutation. Mutation implies the generation of random changes in genes. Such random changes can significantly improve the population. Therefore, the number of mutations should be increased if the population suffers from evolutionary degradation.

Thus, we can formulate the following rule:

- We decrease the mutation probability, if the population improves.
- We increase the mutation probability, if the population degrades.

12.4 Evolutionary dead-end and premature termination of the genetic algorithm

Until now, we have considered only two ways of stopping the genetic algorithm flow. In first, the maximum number of generations has been reached. In second, an acceptable solution has been found. But what if, for a long time, the best solution has not improved in either of the ways? What if we have increased the population size, the probability of mutation, and the probability of crossover, but nothing helps, and perhaps a better solution cannot be found, or perhaps what has already been found is the best, and there is no point in looking for something else?

Let's examine the genetic algorithm progress of the traveling salesman problem, `ch12/ga_dead_end.py`:

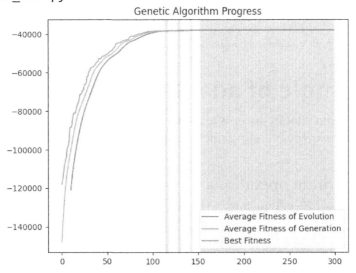

***Figure 12.2:** Genetic Algorithm Progress*

In the preceding *figure 12.2*, we can see that after 150 generations, the best solution to the algorithm stops changing, but we keep trying to find it for another 150 generations. Although it could have prevented the search much earlier, thereby significantly saving the speed of the algorithm. This approach can drastically reduce the speed of the genetic algorithm.

As an exit from the evolutionary cycle, the following rule can be used: *if the best solution does not change during N populations, then exit the cycle.*

So genetic algorithm flow can be represented as shown in the following *figure 12.3:*

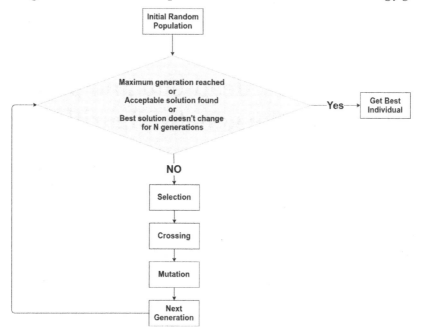

Figure 12.3: *Genetic Algorithm Flow with Premature Termination*

12.5 Example of adaptive genetic algorithm

Now, let's try to put all the concepts together, and build an adaptive genetic algorithm using the example of the traveling salesman problem, ch12/ga_adaptive_example. py.

Genetic algorithm operations

We will use fitness driven ordered crossover, fitness driven shift mutation, and rank selection with elite:

```
def crossover(parent1, parent2):
    return crossover_fitness_driven_order(parent1, parent2)
```

```
def mutate(ind):
    return mutation_fitness_driven_shift(ind)

def selection(population):
    return selection_rank_with_elite(population, elite_size = 1)
```

Genetic algorithm parameters

- We set initial, maximum and minimum population size. We define the boundaries for the population size:

```
POPULATION_SIZE = 200

MIN_POPULATION_SIZE = 50

MAX_POPULATION_SIZE = 300
```

- Initial and minimum crossover probability:

```
CROSSOVER_PROBABILITY = .5

MIN_CROSSOVER_PROBABILITY = .1
```

- Initial and minimum mutation probability:

```
MUTATION_PROBABILITY = .5

MIN_MUTATION_PROBABILITY = .1
```

- Minimum and maximum generations:

```
MAX_GENERATIONS = 10_000

MIN_GENERATIONS = 100
```

Genetic algorithm flow

- **Data collectors:**

```
fit_avg = []
fit_best = []
impr_list = []
ev_avg = []
population_size = []
mutation_prob = []
crossover_prob = []
```

- **Initialization:**

```
generation_num = 0
first_population = [generate_random(len(points))
```

```
                    for _ in range(POPULATION_SIZE)]
best_ind = random.choice(first_population)
population = first_population.copy()
```

- **We stop genetic algorithm cycle if the best fitness value does not differ from the average over 50 generations by 0.1%:**

```
while generation_num < MIN_GENERATIONS or\
        (generation_num < MAX_GENERATIONS and
         is_improvement_positive(fit_best, 50, .001)):
```

- **Genetic algorithm operations:**

```
    generation_num += 1
    offspring = selection(population)
    crossed_offspring = crossover_operation(offspring, crossover,
CROSSOVER_PROBABILITY)
    mutated_offspring = mutation_operation(crossed_offspring,
mutate, MUTATION_PROBABILITY)
    population = mutated_offspring.copy()
    best_ind, fit_avg, fit_best = stats(population, best_ind, fit_
avg, fit_best)
    ev_avg.append(average(fit_avg, 10))
    impr_rate = is_improvement_positive(fit_avg, 10, .001)
    impr_list.append(impr_rate)
```

- **If the population degrades, we increase mutation and crossover probability, and add two random individuals to the population:**

```
    if not impr_rate:
        MUTATION_PROBABILITY = min(MUTATION_PROBABILITY * 1.1, 1)
        CROSSOVER_PROBABILITY = min(CROSSOVER_PROBABILITY * 1.1,
1)
        if len(population) < MAX_POPULATION_SIZE:
            population = population + \
                    [generate_random(len(points)) for _ in
range(2)]
```

- **And if the population improves, we decrease mutation and crossover probability, and remove the worst individual from the population:**

```
else:
    MUTATION_PROBABILITY = max(MUTATION_PROBABILITY * .99,
MIN_MUTATION_PROBABILITY)

    CROSSOVER_PROBABILITY = max(CROSSOVER_PROBABILITY * .99,
MIN_CROSSOVER_PROBABILITY)

    if len(population) > MIN_POPULATION_SIZE:

        worst_ind = min(population, key = lambda ind: ind.
fitness)

        population.remove(worst_ind)
```

Result

Let's examine the results. Refer to the following *figure 12.4:*

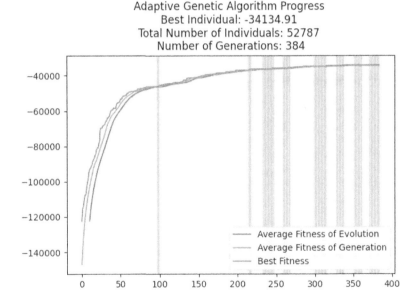

Figure 12.4: Adaptive Genetic Algorithm Flow

Adaptive genetic algorithm found a pretty nice solution – 34,134, very close to the best, 33,523, using only 52787 individuals in whole evolution.

Let's take a look at how the algorithm has adapted its parameters during evolution. Refer to the following *figure 12.5:*

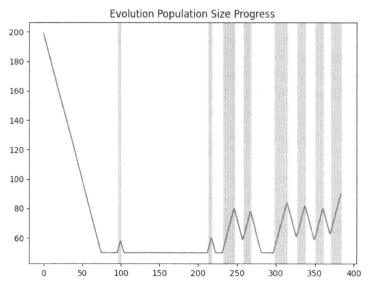

Figure 12.5: *Adaptive Population Size*

As we can see in the preceding figure, algorithm works as expected; it decreases population size in improvement areas and increases in degradation areas.

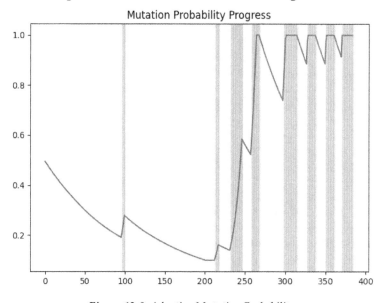

Figure 12.6: *Adaptive Mutation Probability*

The preceding *figure 12.6* shows that mutation adapts quickly on degradation intervals.

12.6 Adaptive genetic algorithm versus Classical genetic algorithm

So, we studied the principle of constructing an adaptive genetic algorithm, and even built an example that showed promising results. But does the introduction of adaptive techniques into a genetic algorithm make any practical sense? Do these techniques make it better than the classical genetic algorithm?

Let's try to compare adaptive and classical genetic algorithms using Monte Carlo simulation. We run each algorithm 100 times on the same dataset and compare the results, ch12/ga_adaptive_vs_classical.py.

Take a look at the following *figure 12.7*:

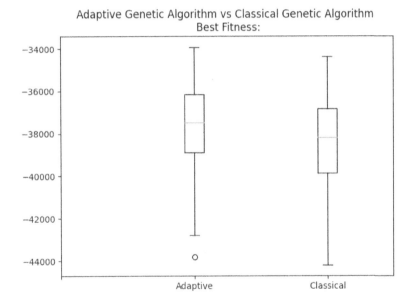

Figure 12.7: *Adaptive Genetic Algorithm vs Classical Genetic Algorithm*

Best Fitness

Yes, as you can see on the preceding figure, the adaptive genetic algorithm shows better results than the classical one. The average result of the adaptive genetic algorithm is -37.528, and for the classic one, it is -38.428. This is a significant difference, keeping in mind that the maximum value for this problem is -33.523.

But this is only one indicator. Let's compare the number of individuals that participate in the evolution of each of the algorithms. Take a look at the following *figure 12.8:*

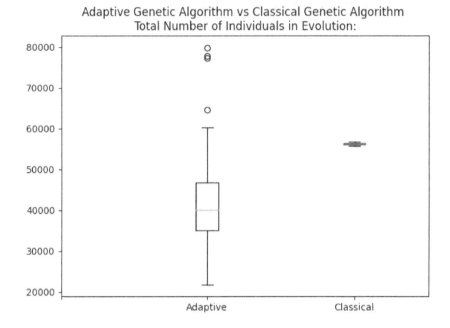

Figure 12.8: Adaptive Genetic Algorithm vs Classical Genetic Algorithm.

Total Number of Individuals

In the preceding figure, we can see an apparent difference between the adaptive and the classic algorithm. The adaptive genetic algorithm uses 1.5 times fewer individuals in evolution than the classical one. This means that the adaptive algorithm is 1.5 times faster than the classic one.

Conclusion

In this chapter, we have explored an inspiring way to modify a genetic algorithm. We have shown that an adaptive genetic algorithm is more likely to find the best result, and it also does it faster. Adaptive genetic algorithms are of great practical interest. Not only because they find a better result than the classic one in a shorter time, but also because they prevent the developer and the scientist from the tedious procedure of selecting the parameters of the genetic algorithm .

In the next chapter, we will explore various technical techniques that can dramatically speed up the genetic algorithm without changing its logic.

Points to remember

- Increase population size when population improves, and decrease population size if population degrades.

- Increase mutation and crossover probability when population improves, and decrease mutation and crossover probability if population degrades.

- Stop evolution cycle if there is no improvement for a significant time.

Questions

1. **Fitness driven mutation method** accepts `max_tries` as a parameter, which determines the number of attempts to find a useful mutation. Let's consider this parameter as a parameter of the genetic algorithm. How should this parameter change when the population is improving and when the population is degrading?

2. **Selection with elite method** accepts `elite_size` as a parameter, which determines the number of best individuals being selected apriori. Let's consider this parameter as a parameter of the genetic algorithm. How should this parameter change when the population is improving and when the population is degrading?

Key terms

- **Adaptive Genetic Algorithm:** Genetic algorithm which adjust its parameters during evolution cycles.

- **Evolutionary Improvement:** When average population fitness grows.

- **Evolutionary Degradation:** When there is no evolutionary improvement.

## CHAPTER 13

Improving Performance

In the previous chapter, we observed the construction of adaptive genetic algorithms. This approach can significantly improve the quality of the solution and the speed of the genetic algorithm. As we already understand, the genetic algorithm's speed is crucial for the possibility of practical application. In this chapter, we will look at purely technical ways to speed up the genetic algorithm that will make the genetic algorithm run even faster.

Structure

In this chapter, we will cover the following topics:

- Calculate fitness function once
- Fitness function caching
- Coarsening values of genes
- Parallel computing
- Population snapshot

Objectives

The main objective of this chapter is to explain the basic principles of acceleration of genetic algorithm execution.

13.1 Calculating fitness function once

As we already know, the calculation of the fitness function is the most resource-intensive operation. Therefore, a fast genetic algorithm should be designed, so that the fitness function is calculated only once for each individual. For example, calculating a fitness function can occur during the initialization of an individual's object and saved to some property.

You've probably noticed that we have already used this approach in our practical examples.

Implementation of fitness function calculation

Here again, we show a trivial implementation of fitness function calculation:

```python
class Individual:

    @classmethod
    def set_fitness_function(cls, fun):
        cls.fitness_function = fun

    def __init__(self, gene_list) -> None:
        self.gene_list = gene_list
        self.fitness = self.__class__.fitness_function(gene_list)
```

13.2 Fitness function caching

In genetic algorithms, individuals with the same gene values can very often arise during evolution. For example, the offspring of two different parents' pairs may be children with the same gene values.

Take a look at the following *figure 13.1:*

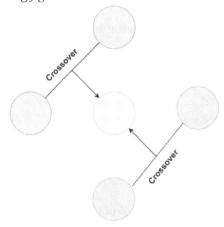

Figure 13.1: When two different pairs of parents generates same individual

Also, mutations of different individuals can lead to individuals with the same gene values. Refer to the following *figure 13.2:*

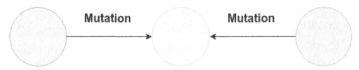

Figure 13.2: *When two different individuals mutate to same individual*

As we already mentioned, the most resource-intensive operation is the calculation of the fitness function. Therefore, it is an obvious step to not calculate the individuals' fitness function with the same set of genes twice. We can make a caching mechanism to reduce the number of fitness function calculations.

Implementation of fitness function caching

Let's study the most straightforward implementation of caching using the schedule problem from *Chapter 9: Combinatorial Optimization – Binary Encoding*.

An individual with fitness function caching can be represented in the following way, ch13/caching/individual.py:

```python
class Individual:
    cache = {}
    cache_hit = 0
    counter = 0
    period = 0
    employees = 0

    @classmethod
    def set_fitness_function(cls, fun):
        cls.fitness_function = fun

    def __init__(self, gene_list) -> None:
        self.gene_list = gene_list
        gene_hash = ''.join([str(g) for g in gene_list])
        cache = self.__class__.cache
        if gene_hash not in cache.keys():
            cache[gene_hash] =\
                self.__class__.fitness_function(self.create_schedule())
        else:
            self.__class__.cache_hit += 1
```

```
self.fitness = cache[gene_hash]
self.__class__.counter += 1
```

And if we run genetic algorithm with fitness function caching, ch13/caching/ga_ with_caching.py:

Total Number of Individuals: 4968

Cache Hits: 1679

As we can see, about a third part of the individuals from the entire history of evolution have the same genes. This means that thanks to caching in the process of evolution, we calculated the fitness function in two cases out of three. This fact can significantly speed up the work of the genetic algorithm.

13.3 Coarsening values of genes

We often do not need to find a very accurate solution in problems that use real gene encoding. For example, if we are looking for the optimal length of a yacht that would satisfy certain conditions, we planned the design case with a centimeter's accuracy, because it is physically rather difficult to build a yacht with greater precision.

So, how can gene values coarsening help? And the fact that after coarsening the values of the genes, we automatically increase the likelihood of the appearance of genes with the same values and thereby make the application of the caching fitness function approach much more effectively.

Take a look at the following *figure 13.3*:

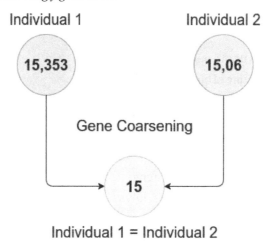

Figure 13.3: Coarsening values of genes

Implementation of gene coarsening

Let's study the straightforward implementation of gene coarsening, `ch13/coarse/individual.py`:

```python
class Individual:
    cache = {}
    cache_hit = 0
    counter = 0

    @classmethod
    def set_fitness_function(cls, fun):
        cls.fitness_function = fun

    def __init__(self, gene_list) -> None:
        coarsed_gene_list = [round(g) for g in gene_list]
        self.gene_list = coarsed_gene_list
        gene_hash = ','.join([str(g) for g in coarsed_gene_list])
        cache = self.__class__.cache
        if gene_hash not in cache.keys():
            cache[gene_hash] =\
                self.__class__.fitness_function(coarsed_gene_list)
        else:
            self.__class__.cache_hit += 1

        self.fitness = cache[gene_hash]
        self.__class__.counter += 1
```

13.4 Parallel computing

One of the most useful things about genetic algorithms is the ability to parallelize computations. The process of evolution comes from a set of atomic operations of crossover and mutation, which are not related. This feature allows you to parallelize the evolutionary process into several threads, processes, or machines, which significantly accelerates the evolutionary process.

We can parallelize crossover operations by processing each pair of parents in a separate process. Take a look at the following *figure 13.4:*

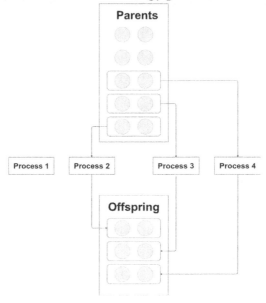

Figure 13.4: Crossover Parallelization

We can use the same approach to parallelize mutation operations, as shown in the following *figure 13.5:*

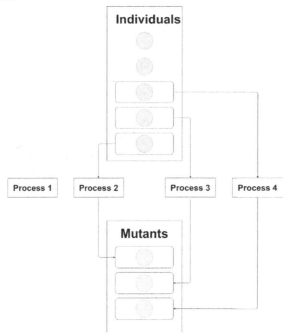

Figure 13.5: Mutation Parallelization

NOTE: We don't only parallelize crossover and mutation, but also the creation of new individuals, hence calculating the fitness function. This is exactly what allows us to speed up the process of evolution.

Implementation of genetic algorithm parallelization

Let's take a look at the radar problem from *Chapter 9: Combinatorial Optimization – Binary Gene Encoding*, one of the most resource-intensive problems we've encountered.

We can parallelize crossover computations as follows, `ch13/parallel/toolbox.py`:

```python
from multiprocessing.pool import Pool

def create_pool():
    return Pool(processes = 4)

def crossover_operation(population, method, prob):
    pool = create_pool()
    crossed_offspring = []
    to_cross = []
    result = []
    for ind1, ind2 in zip(population[::2], population[1::2]):
        if random.random() < prob:
            to_cross.extend([ind1, ind2])
        else:
            crossed_offspring.extend([ind1, ind2])
    for i in range(0, len(to_cross), 2):
        result.append(
            pool.apply_async(method, args = (to_cross[i], to_cross[i +
1]))
        )
    pool.close()
    pool.join()
    for r in result:
        crossed_offspring.extend(r.get())
    return crossed_offspring
```

And the same way for mutation:

```python
def mutation_operation(population, method, prob):
    pool = create_pool()
```

```
mutated_offspring = []
to_mutate = []
result = []
for ind in population:
    if random.random() < prob:
        to_mutate.append(ind)
    else:
        mutated_offspring.append(ind)
for ind in to_mutate:
    result.append(pool.apply_async(method, args = (ind,)))
pool.close()
pool.join()
for r in result:
    mutated_offspring.append(r.get())
return mutated_offspring
```

Now you can check that the parallelized version of genetic algorithm for radar problem is at least two times faster than the single-threaded one.

Tested on HP Probook 450G Intel Core I5 (4 CPUs):

- **Parallel:** 20min 13sec (Script: ch13/parallel/ga_parallel.py)
- **Single:** 47min 55sec (Script: ch9/radar/ga_modified.py)

Of course, the actual increase in speed depends on the particular device's characteristics on which this example will be executed. This approach will give acceleration only if the device contains two or more CPUs.

The same approach can be used to parallelize the computation process across multiple machines. This kind of horizontal scaling can dramatically speed up the process of finding solutions. The ability to scale out the evolutionary process of a genetic algorithm is a remarkable feature of this solution-seeking method, unlike other methods that are forced to run in a single-thread mode.

13.5 Population snapshot

Let's say we have some scientific problem that we can solve using a genetic algorithm. The algorithm's estimated running time will take about a week, which is an acceptable time. And on the fifth day of the algorithm's execution, a critical situation arises that provokes a reboot of the whole system on which the algorithm is executed. So, what now? Start all over again?! What if something bad happens again that prevents the algorithm's completion?

In general, the probability of an unexpected situation in the operating system running for a long time is relatively high, so it would be ideal to have a way to continue the work of the genetic algorithm from the point of stopping, and not from the very beginning.

We will study a method of storing the population of a generation in some storage. Then, we can restore the last population and continue with the evolution.

Take a look at the following *figure 13.6:*

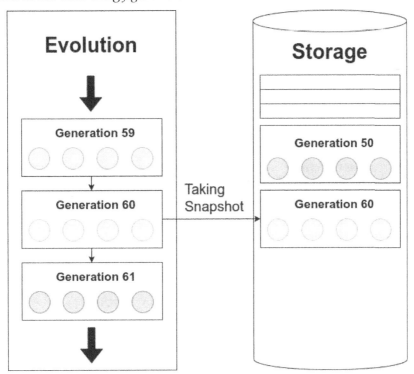

Figure 13.6: *Taking Generation Snapshots*

In general, the process of storing a population snapshot of generation can take some time; so it is better not to store all generations in a row. For example, you can take population snapshots on each – tenth, twentieth, or fiftieth generation.

> **NOTE: A fair question may arise – Why is this approach being studied in the chapter dedicated to performance improving? In fact, for the algorithm working on big data problems, unexpected situations that lead to the execution stop of the genetic algorithm occur very often. Therefore, the ability to restore execution from a certain checkpoint dramatically speeds up the process of finding a solution.**

Implementation of population snapshot management

Here, we will show a trivial implementation of taking population snapshots, ch13/snapshot/individual.py.

We define the general individual:

```python
class Individual:
    def __init__(self, gene_list) -> None:
        self.gene_list = gene_list
```

Population dump function:

```python
def dump_population(population, path):
    ind_genes = [ind.gene_list for ind in population]
    with open(path, 'w') as f:
        json.dump(ind_genes, f)
```

Population restore function:

```python
def restore_population(path):
    population = []
    with open(path) as json_file:
        ind_genes = json.load(json_file)
        for gene_list in ind_genes:
            population.append(Individual(gene_list))
    return population
```

And an example of usage:

```python
if __name__ == '__main__':
    population = [Individual([random.randint(0, 100)]) for _ in range(100)]
    path = '/tmp/population_genes.json'
    dump_population(population, path)
    restored_population = restore_population(path)
```

Conclusion

This chapter has investigated the basic and relatively simple and technical ways to speed up genetic algorithms. In addition to the methods that we have studied, a critical acceleration method is helpful in optimizing the fitness function calculation. But the analysis of the fitness function depends on a specific task. Therefore, general mechanisms for its acceleration cannot be given.

It is important to understand that even if the genetic algorithm's implementation is without acceleration, the methods show acceptable results. You should still try to optimize the genetic algorithm, because in case of fast genetic algorithm, we will be able to afford a more thorough search within the same time of work. For example, we can then use not just 100 individuals for the population, but 200 individuals. And as we already know, an increase in the population very often increases the likelihood of finding a better solution.

Index

Made in the USA
Monee, IL
10 June 2022

97801030R00149